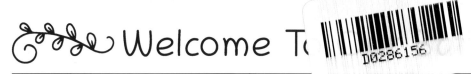

Welcome To ...room

Rate your experience

Seat comfort ☆☆☆☆☆

Flush strength ☆☆☆☆☆

Ambience ☆☆☆☆☆

Paper quality ☆☆☆☆☆

Amenities ☆☆☆☆☆

Sound proofing ☆☆☆☆☆

Name: _____ Visiting from: _____

Date: _____ Time: _____ Duration: _____

Describe our bathroom in one word: _____

Do you scrunch or fold? Why? _____

Most memorable bathroom visited? _____

Best euphemism for performing #2? _____

Favorite bathroom activity: _____

Doodles & brilliant bathroom thoughts

During your visit did you

☐ Look in the medicine cabinet

☐ Check out your butt in the mirror

☐ Flush to cover up pooping sounds

☐ Reply to work emails / messages

☐ Scroll through social media

☐ Act to prevent any splashback

☐ Read through the entire guest book

Welcome To Our Bathroom

Name: _____ Visiting from: _____

Date: _____ Time: _____ Duration: _____

Describe our bathroom in one word: _____

Do you scrunch or fold? Why? _____

Most memorable bathroom visited? _____

Best euphemism for performing #2? _____

Favorite bathroom activity: _____

Rate your experience

Seat comfort   ☆ ☆ ☆ ☆ ☆

Flush strength   ☆ ☆ ☆ ☆ ☆

Ambience   ☆ ☆ ☆ ☆ ☆

Paper quality   ☆ ☆ ☆ ☆ ☆

Amenities   ☆ ☆ ☆ ☆ ☆

Sound proofing   ☆ ☆ ☆ ☆ ☆

During your visit did you

☐ Look in the medicine cabinet

☐ Check out your butt in the mirror

☐ Flush to cover up pooping sounds

☐ Reply to work emails / messages

☐ Scroll through social media

☐ Act to prevent any splashback

☐ Read through the entire guest book

Doodles & brilliant bathroom thoughts

Welcome To Our Bathroom

Rate your experience

Seat comfort ☆ ☆ ☆ ☆ ☆

Flush strength ☆ ☆ ☆ ☆ ☆

Ambience ☆ ☆ ☆ ☆ ☆

Paper quality ☆ ☆ ☆ ☆ ☆

Amenities ☆ ☆ ☆ ☆ ☆

Sound proofing ☆ ☆ ☆ ☆ ☆

Name: _____ Visiting from: _____

Date: _____ Time: _____ Duration: _____

Describe our bathroom in one word: _____

Do you scrunch or fold? Why? _____

Most memorable bathroom visited? _____

Best euphemism for performing #2? _____

Favorite bathroom activity: _____

Doodles & brilliant bathroom thoughts

During your visit did you

☐ Look in the medicine cabinet

☐ Check out your butt in the mirror

☐ Flush to cover up pooping sounds

☐ Reply to work emails / messages

☐ Scroll through social media

☐ Act to prevent any splashback

☐ Read through the entire guest book

Welcome To Our Bathroom

Name: _____   Visiting from: _____

Date: _____   Time: _____   Duration: _____

Describe our bathroom in one word: _____

Do you scrunch or fold? Why? _____

Most memorable bathroom visited? _____

Best euphemism for performing #2? _____

Favorite bathroom activity: _____

Rate your experience

Seat comfort ☆ ☆ ☆ ☆ ☆

Flush strength ☆ ☆ ☆ ☆ ☆

Ambience ☆ ☆ ☆ ☆ ☆

Paper quality ☆ ☆ ☆ ☆ ☆

Amenities ☆ ☆ ☆ ☆ ☆

Sound proofing ☆ ☆ ☆ ☆ ☆

During your visit did you

☐ Look in the medicine cabinet

☐ Check out your butt in the mirror

☐ Flush to cover up pooping sounds

☐ Reply to work emails / messages

☐ Scroll through social media

☐ Act to prevent any splashback

☐ Read through the entire guest book

Doodles & brilliant bathroom thoughts

Welcome To Our Bathroom

Rate your experience

Seat comfort ☆ ☆ ☆ ☆ ☆

Flush strength ☆ ☆ ☆ ☆ ☆

Ambience ☆ ☆ ☆ ☆ ☆

Paper quality ☆ ☆ ☆ ☆ ☆

Amenities ☆ ☆ ☆ ☆ ☆

Sound proofing ☆ ☆ ☆ ☆ ☆

Name: _____ Visiting from: _____

Date: _____ Time: _____ Duration: _____

Describe our bathroom in one word: _____

Do you scrunch or fold? Why? _____

Most memorable bathroom visited? _____

Best euphemism for performing #2? _____

Favorite bathroom activity: _____

Doodles & brilliant bathroom thoughts

During your visit did you

☐ Look in the medicine cabinet

☐ Check out your butt in the mirror

☐ Flush to cover up pooping sounds

☐ Reply to work emails / messages

☐ Scroll through social media

☐ Act to prevent any splashback

☐ Read through the entire guest book

Welcome To Our Bathroom

| Name: | Visiting from: | |
| Date: | Time: | Duration: |

Describe our bathroom in one word: _____

Do you scrunch or fold? Why? _____

Most memorable bathroom visited? _____

Best euphemism for performing #2? _____

Favorite bathroom activity: _____

Rate your experience

Seat comfort	☆ ☆ ☆ ☆ ☆
Flush strength	☆ ☆ ☆ ☆ ☆
Ambience	☆ ☆ ☆ ☆ ☆
Paper quality	☆ ☆ ☆ ☆ ☆
Amenities	☆ ☆ ☆ ☆ ☆
Sound proofing	☆ ☆ ☆ ☆ ☆

During your visit did you

- ☐ Look in the medicine cabinet
- ☐ Check out your butt in the mirror
- ☐ Flush to cover up pooping sounds
- ☐ Reply to work emails / messages
- ☐ Scroll through social media
- ☐ Act to prevent any splashback
- ☐ Read through the entire guest book

Doodles & brilliant bathroom thoughts

Welcome To Our Bathroom

Rate your experience

Seat comfort	☆ ☆ ☆ ☆ ☆
Flush strength	☆ ☆ ☆ ☆ ☆
Ambience	☆ ☆ ☆ ☆ ☆
Paper quality	☆ ☆ ☆ ☆ ☆
Amenities	☆ ☆ ☆ ☆ ☆
Sound proofing	☆ ☆ ☆ ☆ ☆

Name: _____ Visiting from: _____

Date: _____ Time: _____ Duration: _____

Describe our bathroom in one word: _____

Do you scrunch or fold? Why? _____

Most memorable bathroom visited? _____

Best euphemism for performing #2? _____

Favorite bathroom activity: _____

Doodles & brilliant bathroom thoughts

During your visit did you

☐ Look in the medicine cabinet

☐ Check out your butt in the mirror

☐ Flush to cover up pooping sounds

☐ Reply to work emails / messages

☐ Scroll through social media

☐ Act to prevent any splashback

☐ Read through the entire guest book

Welcome To Our Bathroom

Name: _____ Visiting from: _____

Date: _____ Time: _____ Duration: _____

Describe our bathroom in one word: _____

Do you scrunch or fold? Why? _____

Most memorable bathroom visited? _____

Best euphemism for performing #2? _____

Favorite bathroom activity: _____

Rate your experience

Seat comfort ☆ ☆ ☆ ☆ ☆

Flush strength ☆ ☆ ☆ ☆ ☆

Ambience ☆ ☆ ☆ ☆ ☆

Paper quality ☆ ☆ ☆ ☆ ☆

Amenities ☆ ☆ ☆ ☆ ☆

Sound proofing ☆ ☆ ☆ ☆ ☆

During your visit did you

☐ Look in the medicine cabinet

☐ Check out your butt in the mirror

☐ Flush to cover up pooping sounds

☐ Reply to work emails / messages

☐ Scroll through social media

☐ Act to prevent any splashback

☐ Read through the entire guest book

Doodles & brilliant bathroom thoughts

Welcome To Our Bathroom

Rate your experience

Seat comfort ☆☆☆☆☆

Flush strength ☆☆☆☆☆

Ambience ☆☆☆☆☆

Paper quality ☆☆☆☆☆

Amenities ☆☆☆☆☆

Sound proofing ☆☆☆☆☆

Name: _____ Visiting from: _____

Date: _____ Time: _____ Duration: _____

Describe our bathroom in one word: _____

Do you scrunch or fold? Why? _____

Most memorable bathroom visited? _____

Best euphemism for performing #2? _____

Favorite bathroom activity: _____

Doodles & brilliant bathroom thoughts

During your visit did you

☐ Look in the medicine cabinet

☐ Check out your butt in the mirror

☐ Flush to cover up pooping sounds

☐ Reply to work emails / messages

☐ Scroll through social media

☐ Act to prevent any splashback

☐ Read through the entire guest book

Welcome To Our Bathroom

Name: Visiting from:

Date: Time: Duration:

Rate your experience

Seat comfort ☆ ☆ ☆ ☆ ☆

Flush strength ☆ ☆ ☆ ☆ ☆

Ambience ☆ ☆ ☆ ☆ ☆

Paper quality ☆ ☆ ☆ ☆ ☆

Amenities ☆ ☆ ☆ ☆ ☆

Sound proofing ☆ ☆ ☆ ☆ ☆

Describe our bathroom in one word: _____

Do you scrunch or fold? Why? _____

Most memorable bathroom visited? _____

Best euphemism for performing #2? _____

Favorite bathroom activity: _____

During your visit did you

- ☐ Look in the medicine cabinet
- ☐ Check out your butt in the mirror
- ☐ Flush to cover up pooping sounds
- ☐ Reply to work emails / messages
- ☐ Scroll through social media
- ☐ Act to prevent any splashback
- ☐ Read through the entire guest book

Doodles & brilliant bathroom thoughts

Welcome To Our Bathroom

Rate your experience

Seat comfort	☆ ☆ ☆ ☆ ☆
Flush strength	☆ ☆ ☆ ☆ ☆
Ambience	☆ ☆ ☆ ☆ ☆
Paper quality	☆ ☆ ☆ ☆ ☆
Amenities	☆ ☆ ☆ ☆ ☆
Sound proofing	☆ ☆ ☆ ☆ ☆

Name: _____ Visiting from: _____

Date: _____ Time: _____ Duration: _____

Describe our bathroom in one word: _____

Do you scrunch or fold? Why? _____

Most memorable bathroom visited? _____

Best euphemism for performing #2? _____

Favorite bathroom activity: _____

Doodles & brilliant bathroom thoughts

During your visit did you

☐ Look in the medicine cabinet

☐ Check out your butt in the mirror

☐ Flush to cover up pooping sounds

☐ Reply to work emails / messages

☐ Scroll through social media

☐ Act to prevent any splashback

☐ Read through the entire guest book

Welcome To Our Bathroom

Name: _____ Visiting from: _____

Date: _____ Time: _____ Duration: _____

Describe our bathroom in one word: _____

Do you scrunch or fold? Why? _____

Most memorable bathroom visited? _____

Best euphemism for performing #2? _____

Favorite bathroom activity: _____

Rate your experience

Seat comfort ☆ ☆ ☆ ☆ ☆

Flush strength ☆ ☆ ☆ ☆ ☆

Ambience ☆ ☆ ☆ ☆ ☆

Paper quality ☆ ☆ ☆ ☆ ☆

Amenities ☆ ☆ ☆ ☆ ☆

Sound proofing ☆ ☆ ☆ ☆ ☆

During your visit did you

☐ Look in the medicine cabinet

☐ Check out your butt in the mirror

☐ Flush to cover up pooping sounds

☐ Reply to work emails / messages

☐ Scroll through social media

☐ Act to prevent any splashback

☐ Read through the entire guest book

Doodles & brilliant bathroom thoughts

Welcome To Our Bathroom

Rate your experience

Seat comfort ☆ ☆ ☆ ☆ ☆

Flush strength ☆ ☆ ☆ ☆ ☆

Ambience ☆ ☆ ☆ ☆ ☆

Paper quality ☆ ☆ ☆ ☆ ☆

Amenities ☆ ☆ ☆ ☆ ☆

Sound proofing ☆ ☆ ☆ ☆ ☆

Name: _____ Visiting from: _____

Date: _____ Time: _____ Duration: _____

Describe our bathroom in one word: _____

Do you scrunch or fold? Why? _____

Most memorable bathroom visited? _____

Best euphemism for performing #2? _____

Favorite bathroom activity: _____

Doodles & brilliant bathroom thoughts

During your visit did you

☐ Look in the medicine cabinet

☐ Check out your butt in the mirror

☐ Flush to cover up pooping sounds

☐ Reply to work emails / messages

☐ Scroll through social media

☐ Act to prevent any splashback

☐ Read through the entire guest book

Welcome To Our Bathroom

Name: _____ Visiting from: _____

Date: _____ Time: _____ Duration: _____

Describe our bathroom in one word: _____

Do you scrunch or fold? Why? _____

Most memorable bathroom visited? _____

Best euphemism for performing #2? _____

Favorite bathroom activity: _____

Rate your experience

Seat comfort	☆	☆	☆	☆	☆
Flush strength	☆	☆	☆	☆	☆
Ambience	☆	☆	☆	☆	☆
Paper quality	☆	☆	☆	☆	☆
Amenities	☆	☆	☆	☆	☆
Sound proofing	☆	☆	☆	☆	☆

During your visit did you

☐ Look in the medicine cabinet

☐ Check out your butt in the mirror

☐ Flush to cover up pooping sounds

☐ Reply to work emails / messages

☐ Scroll through social media

☐ Act to prevent any splashback

☐ Read through the entire guest book

Doodles & brilliant bathroom thoughts

Welcome To Our Bathroom

Rate your experience

Seat comfort ☆ ☆ ☆ ☆ ☆

Flush strength ☆ ☆ ☆ ☆ ☆

Ambience ☆ ☆ ☆ ☆ ☆

Paper quality ☆ ☆ ☆ ☆ ☆

Amenities ☆ ☆ ☆ ☆ ☆

Sound proofing ☆ ☆ ☆ ☆ ☆

Name: _____ Visiting from: _____

Date: _____ Time: _____ Duration: _____

Describe our bathroom in one word: _____

Do you scrunch or fold? Why? _____

Most memorable bathroom visited? _____

Best euphemism for performing #2? _____

Favorite bathroom activity: _____

Doodles & brilliant bathroom thoughts

During your visit did you

☐ Look in the medicine cabinet

☐ Check out your butt in the mirror

☐ Flush to cover up pooping sounds

☐ Reply to work emails / messages

☐ Scroll through social media

☐ Act to prevent any splashback

☐ Read through the entire guest book

Welcome To Our Bathroom

Name: Visiting from:

Date: Time: Duration:

Describe our bathroom in one word: _____

Do you scrunch or fold? Why? _____

Most memorable bathroom visited? _____

Best euphemism for performing #2? _____

Favorite bathroom activity: _____

Rate your experience

Seat comfort   ☆ ☆ ☆ ☆ ☆

Flush strength   ☆ ☆ ☆ ☆ ☆

Ambience   ☆ ☆ ☆ ☆ ☆

Paper quality   ☆ ☆ ☆ ☆ ☆

Amenities   ☆ ☆ ☆ ☆ ☆

Sound proofing ☆ ☆ ☆ ☆ ☆

During your visit did you

☐ Look in the medicine cabinet

☐ Check out your butt in the mirror

☐ Flush to cover up pooping sounds

☐ Reply to work emails / messages

☐ Scroll through social media

☐ Act to prevent any splashback

☐ Read through the entire guest book

Doodles & brilliant bathroom thoughts

Welcome To Our Bathroom

Rate your experience

Seat comfort	☆ ☆ ☆ ☆ ☆
Flush strength	☆ ☆ ☆ ☆ ☆
Ambience	☆ ☆ ☆ ☆ ☆
Paper quality	☆ ☆ ☆ ☆ ☆
Amenities	☆ ☆ ☆ ☆ ☆
Sound proofing	☆ ☆ ☆ ☆ ☆

Name: _____   Visiting from: _____

Date: _____   Time: _____   Duration: _____

Describe our bathroom in one word: _____

Do you scrunch or fold? Why? _____

Most memorable bathroom visited? _____

Best euphemism for performing #2? _____

Favorite bathroom activity: _____

Doodles & brilliant bathroom thoughts

During your visit did you

☐ Look in the medicine cabinet

☐ Check out your butt in the mirror

☐ Flush to cover up pooping sounds

☐ Reply to work emails / messages

☐ Scroll through social media

☐ Act to prevent any splashback

☐ Read through the entire guest book

Welcome To Our Bathroom

Name: Visiting from:

Date: Time: Duration:

Describe our bathroom in one word: _____

Do you scrunch or fold? Why? _____

Most memorable bathroom visited? _____

Best euphemism for performing #2? _____

Favorite bathroom activity: _____

Rate your experience

Seat comfort	☆ ☆ ☆ ☆ ☆
Flush strength	☆ ☆ ☆ ☆ ☆
Ambience	☆ ☆ ☆ ☆ ☆
Paper quality	☆ ☆ ☆ ☆ ☆
Amenities	☆ ☆ ☆ ☆ ☆
Sound proofing	☆ ☆ ☆ ☆ ☆

During your visit did you

☐ Look in the medicine cabinet

☐ Check out your butt in the mirror

☐ Flush to cover up pooping sounds

☐ Reply to work emails / messages

☐ Scroll through social media

☐ Act to prevent any splashback

☐ Read through the entire guest book

Doodles & brilliant bathroom thoughts

Welcome To Our Bathroom

Rate your experience

Seat comfort ☆☆☆☆☆

Flush strength ☆☆☆☆☆

Ambience ☆☆☆☆☆

Paper quality ☆☆☆☆☆

Amenities ☆☆☆☆☆

Sound proofing ☆☆☆☆☆

Name: _____ Visiting from: _____

Date: _____ Time: _____ Duration: _____

Describe our bathroom in one word: _____

Do you scrunch or fold? Why? _____

Most memorable bathroom visited? _____

Best euphemism for performing #2? _____

Favorite bathroom activity: _____

Doodles & brilliant bathroom thoughts

During your visit did you

☐ Look in the medicine cabinet

☐ Check out your butt in the mirror

☐ Flush to cover up pooping sounds

☐ Reply to work emails / messages

☐ Scroll through social media

☐ Act to prevent any splashback

☐ Read through the entire guest book

Welcome To Our Bathroom

Name: _____   Visiting from: _____

Date: _____   Time: _____   Duration: _____

Describe our bathroom in one word: _____

Do you scrunch or fold? Why? _____

Most memorable bathroom visited? _____

Best euphemism for performing #2? _____

Favorite bathroom activity: _____

Rate your experience

Seat comfort ☆ ☆ ☆ ☆ ☆

Flush strength ☆ ☆ ☆ ☆ ☆

Ambience ☆ ☆ ☆ ☆ ☆

Paper quality ☆ ☆ ☆ ☆ ☆

Amenities ☆ ☆ ☆ ☆ ☆

Sound proofing ☆ ☆ ☆ ☆ ☆

During your visit did you

☐ Look in the medicine cabinet

☐ Check out your butt in the mirror

☐ Flush to cover up pooping sounds

☐ Reply to work emails / messages

☐ Scroll through social media

☐ Act to prevent any splashback

☐ Read through the entire guest book

Doodles & brilliant bathroom thoughts

Welcome To Our Bathroom

Rate your experience

Seat comfort ☆☆☆☆☆

Flush strength ☆☆☆☆☆

Ambience ☆☆☆☆☆

Paper quality ☆☆☆☆☆

Amenities ☆☆☆☆☆

Sound proofing ☆☆☆☆☆

Name: _____ Visiting from: _____

Date: _____ Time: _____ Duration: _____

Describe our bathroom in one word: _____

Do you scrunch or fold? Why? _____

Most memorable bathroom visited? _____

Best euphemism for performing #2? _____

Favorite bathroom activity: _____

Doodles & brilliant bathroom thoughts

During your visit did you

☐ Look in the medicine cabinet

☐ Check out your butt in the mirror

☐ Flush to cover up pooping sounds

☐ Reply to work emails / messages

☐ Scroll through social media

☐ Act to prevent any splashback

☐ Read through the entire guest book

Welcome To Our Bathroom

Name: _____ Visiting from: _____

Date: _____ Time: _____ Duration: _____

Describe our bathroom in one word: _____

Do you scrunch or fold? Why? _____

Most memorable bathroom visited? _____

Best euphemism for performing #2? _____

Favorite bathroom activity: _____

Rate your experience

Seat comfort ☆ ☆ ☆ ☆ ☆

Flush strength ☆ ☆ ☆ ☆ ☆

Ambience ☆ ☆ ☆ ☆ ☆

Paper quality ☆ ☆ ☆ ☆ ☆

Amenities ☆ ☆ ☆ ☆ ☆

Sound proofing ☆ ☆ ☆ ☆ ☆

During your visit did you

☐ Look in the medicine cabinet

☐ Check out your butt in the mirror

☐ Flush to cover up pooping sounds

☐ Reply to work emails / messages

☐ Scroll through social media

☐ Act to prevent any splashback

☐ Read through the entire guest book

Doodles & brilliant bathroom thoughts

Welcome To Our Bathroom

Rate your experience

Seat comfort ☆ ☆ ☆ ☆ ☆

Flush strength ☆ ☆ ☆ ☆ ☆

Ambience ☆ ☆ ☆ ☆ ☆

Paper quality ☆ ☆ ☆ ☆ ☆

Amenities ☆ ☆ ☆ ☆ ☆

Sound proofing ☆ ☆ ☆ ☆ ☆

Name: _____ Visiting from: _____

Date: _____ Time: _____ Duration: _____

Describe our bathroom in one word: _____

Do you scrunch or fold? Why? _____

Most memorable bathroom visited? _____

Best euphemism for performing #2? _____

Favorite bathroom activity: _____

Doodles & brilliant bathroom thoughts

During your visit did you

☐ Look in the medicine cabinet

☐ Check out your butt in the mirror

☐ Flush to cover up pooping sounds

☐ Reply to work emails / messages

☐ Scroll through social media

☐ Act to prevent any splashback

☐ Read through the entire guest book

Welcome To Our Bathroom

Name: _____ Visiting from: _____

Date: _____ Time: _____ Duration: _____

Describe our bathroom in one word: _____

Do you scrunch or fold? Why? _____

Most memorable bathroom visited? _____

Best euphemism for performing #2? _____

Favorite bathroom activity: _____

Rate your experience

Seat comfort ☆ ☆ ☆ ☆ ☆

Flush strength ☆ ☆ ☆ ☆ ☆

Ambience ☆ ☆ ☆ ☆ ☆

Paper quality ☆ ☆ ☆ ☆ ☆

Amenities ☆ ☆ ☆ ☆ ☆

Sound proofing ☆ ☆ ☆ ☆ ☆

During your visit did you

☐ Look in the medicine cabinet

☐ Check out your butt in the mirror

☐ Flush to cover up pooping sounds

☐ Reply to work emails / messages

☐ Scroll through social media

☐ Act to prevent any splashback

☐ Read through the entire guest book

Doodles & brilliant bathroom thoughts

Welcome To Our Bathroom

Rate your experience

Seat comfort	☆ ☆ ☆ ☆ ☆
Flush strength	☆ ☆ ☆ ☆ ☆
Ambience	☆ ☆ ☆ ☆ ☆
Paper quality	☆ ☆ ☆ ☆ ☆
Amenities	☆ ☆ ☆ ☆ ☆
Sound proofing	☆ ☆ ☆ ☆ ☆

Name: _____ Visiting from: _____

Date: _____ Time: _____ Duration: _____

Describe our bathroom in one word: _____

Do you scrunch or fold? Why? _____

Most memorable bathroom visited? _____

Best euphemism for performing #2? _____

Favorite bathroom activity: _____

Doodles & brilliant bathroom thoughts

During your visit did you

☐ Look in the medicine cabinet

☐ Check out your butt in the mirror

☐ Flush to cover up pooping sounds

☐ Reply to work emails / messages

☐ Scroll through social media

☐ Act to prevent any splashback

☐ Read through the entire guest book

Welcome To Our Bathroom

Name: _____   Visiting from: _____

Date: _____   Time: _____   Duration: _____

Describe our bathroom in one word: _____

Do you scrunch or fold? Why? _____

Most memorable bathroom visited? _____

Best euphemism for performing #2? _____

Favorite bathroom activity: _____

Rate your experience

Seat comfort   ☆ ☆ ☆ ☆ ☆

Flush strength ☆ ☆ ☆ ☆ ☆

Ambience   ☆ ☆ ☆ ☆ ☆

Paper quality   ☆ ☆ ☆ ☆ ☆

Amenities   ☆ ☆ ☆ ☆ ☆

Sound proofing ☆ ☆ ☆ ☆ ☆

During your visit did you

☐ Look in the medicine cabinet

☐ Check out your butt in the mirror

☐ Flush to cover up pooping sounds

☐ Reply to work emails / messages

☐ Scroll through social media

☐ Act to prevent any splashback

☐ Read through the entire guest book

Doodles & brilliant bathroom thoughts

Welcome To Our Bathroom

Rate your experience

Seat comfort ☆☆☆☆☆

Flush strength ☆☆☆☆☆

Ambience ☆☆☆☆☆

Paper quality ☆☆☆☆☆

Amenities ☆☆☆☆☆

Sound proofing ☆☆☆☆☆

Name: _____ Visiting from: _____

Date: _____ Time: _____ Duration: _____

Describe our bathroom in one word: _____

Do you scrunch or fold? Why? _____

Most memorable bathroom visited? _____

Best euphemism for performing #2? _____

Favorite bathroom activity: _____

Doodles & brilliant bathroom thoughts

During your visit did you

☐ Look in the medicine cabinet

☐ Check out your butt in the mirror

☐ Flush to cover up pooping sounds

☐ Reply to work emails / messages

☐ Scroll through social media

☐ Act to prevent any splashback

☐ Read through the entire guest book

Welcome To Our Bathroom

Name: _____ Visiting from: _____

Date: _____ Time: _____ Duration: _____

Describe our bathroom in one word: _____

Do you scrunch or fold? Why? _____

Most memorable bathroom visited? _____

Best euphemism for performing #2? _____

Favorite bathroom activity: _____

Rate your experience

Seat comfort ☆ ☆ ☆ ☆ ☆

Flush strength ☆ ☆ ☆ ☆ ☆

Ambience ☆ ☆ ☆ ☆ ☆

Paper quality ☆ ☆ ☆ ☆ ☆

Amenities ☆ ☆ ☆ ☆ ☆

Sound proofing ☆ ☆ ☆ ☆ ☆

During your visit did you

☐ Look in the medicine cabinet

☐ Check out your butt in the mirror

☐ Flush to cover up pooping sounds

☐ Reply to work emails / messages

☐ Scroll through social media

☐ Act to prevent any splashback

☐ Read through the entire guest book

Doodles & brilliant bathroom thoughts

Welcome To Our Bathroom

Rate your experience

Seat comfort	☆ ☆ ☆ ☆ ☆
Flush strength	☆ ☆ ☆ ☆ ☆
Ambience	☆ ☆ ☆ ☆ ☆
Paper quality	☆ ☆ ☆ ☆ ☆
Amenities	☆ ☆ ☆ ☆ ☆
Sound proofing	☆ ☆ ☆ ☆ ☆

Name: _____ Visiting from: _____

Date: _____ Time: _____ Duration: _____

Describe our bathroom in one word: _____

Do you scrunch or fold? Why? _____

Most memorable bathroom visited? _____

Best euphemism for performing #2? _____

Favorite bathroom activity: _____

Doodles & brilliant bathroom thoughts

During your visit did you

☐ Look in the medicine cabinet

☐ Check out your butt in the mirror

☐ Flush to cover up pooping sounds

☐ Reply to work emails / messages

☐ Scroll through social media

☐ Act to prevent any splashback

☐ Read through the entire guest book

Welcome To Our Bathroom

Name: _____ Visiting from: _____

Date: _____ Time: _____ Duration: _____

Describe our bathroom in one word: _____

Do you scrunch or fold? Why? _____

Most memorable bathroom visited? _____

Best euphemism for performing #2? _____

Favorite bathroom activity: _____

Rate your experience

Seat comfort ☆ ☆ ☆ ☆ ☆

Flush strength ☆ ☆ ☆ ☆ ☆

Ambience ☆ ☆ ☆ ☆ ☆

Paper quality ☆ ☆ ☆ ☆ ☆

Amenities ☆ ☆ ☆ ☆ ☆

Sound proofing ☆ ☆ ☆ ☆ ☆

During your visit did you

☐ Look in the medicine cabinet

☐ Check out your butt in the mirror

☐ Flush to cover up pooping sounds

☐ Reply to work emails / messages

☐ Scroll through social media

☐ Act to prevent any splashback

☐ Read through the entire guest book

Doodles & brilliant bathroom thoughts

Welcome To Our Bathroom

Rate your experience

Seat comfort ☆☆☆☆☆

Flush strength ☆☆☆☆☆

Ambience ☆☆☆☆☆

Paper quality ☆☆☆☆☆

Amenities ☆☆☆☆☆

Sound proofing ☆☆☆☆☆

Name: _____ Visiting from: _____

Date: _____ Time: _____ Duration: _____

Describe our bathroom in one word: _____

Do you scrunch or fold? Why? _____

Most memorable bathroom visited? _____

Best euphemism for performing #2? _____

Favorite bathroom activity: _____

Doodles & brilliant bathroom thoughts

During your visit did you

☐ Look in the medicine cabinet

☐ Check out your butt in the mirror

☐ Flush to cover up pooping sounds

☐ Reply to work emails / messages

☐ Scroll through social media

☐ Act to prevent any splashback

☐ Read through the entire guest book

Welcome To Our Bathroom

Name: _____ Visiting from: _____

Date: _____ Time: _____ Duration: _____

Describe our bathroom in one word: _____

Do you scrunch or fold? Why? _____

Most memorable bathroom visited? _____

Best euphemism for performing #2? _____

Favorite bathroom activity: _____

Rate your experience

Seat comfort ☆ ☆ ☆ ☆ ☆

Flush strength ☆ ☆ ☆ ☆ ☆

Ambience ☆ ☆ ☆ ☆ ☆

Paper quality ☆ ☆ ☆ ☆ ☆

Amenities ☆ ☆ ☆ ☆ ☆

Sound proofing ☆ ☆ ☆ ☆ ☆

During your visit did you

☐ Look in the medicine cabinet

☐ Check out your butt in the mirror

☐ Flush to cover up pooping sounds

☐ Reply to work emails / messages

☐ Scroll through social media

☐ Act to prevent any splashback

☐ Read through the entire guest book

Doodles & brilliant bathroom thoughts

Welcome To Our Bathroom

Rate your experience

Seat comfort ☆☆☆☆☆

Flush strength ☆☆☆☆☆

Ambience ☆☆☆☆☆

Paper quality ☆☆☆☆☆

Amenities ☆☆☆☆☆

Sound proofing ☆☆☆☆☆

Name: _____ Visiting from: _____

Date: _____ Time: _____ Duration: _____

Describe our bathroom in one word: _____

Do you scrunch or fold? Why? _____

Most memorable bathroom visited? _____

Best euphemism for performing #2? _____

Favorite bathroom activity: _____

Doodles & brilliant bathroom thoughts

During your visit did you

☐ Look in the medicine cabinet

☐ Check out your butt in the mirror

☐ Flush to cover up pooping sounds

☐ Reply to work emails / messages

☐ Scroll through social media

☐ Act to prevent any splashback

☐ Read through the entire guest book

Welcome To Our Bathroom

Name: _____ Visiting from: _____

Date: _____ Time: _____ Duration: _____

Describe our bathroom in one word: _____

Do you scrunch or fold? Why? _____

Most memorable bathroom visited? _____

Best euphemism for performing #2? _____

Favorite bathroom activity: _____

Rate your experience

Seat comfort	☆ ☆ ☆ ☆ ☆
Flush strength	☆ ☆ ☆ ☆ ☆
Ambience	☆ ☆ ☆ ☆ ☆
Paper quality	☆ ☆ ☆ ☆ ☆
Amenities	☆ ☆ ☆ ☆ ☆
Sound proofing	☆ ☆ ☆ ☆ ☆

During your visit did you

☐ Look in the medicine cabinet

☐ Check out your butt in the mirror

☐ Flush to cover up pooping sounds

☐ Reply to work emails / messages

☐ Scroll through social media

☐ Act to prevent any splashback

☐ Read through the entire guest book

Doodles & brilliant bathroom thoughts

Welcome To Our Bathroom

Rate your experience

Seat comfort ☆☆☆☆☆

Flush strength ☆☆☆☆☆

Ambience ☆☆☆☆☆

Paper quality ☆☆☆☆☆

Amenities ☆☆☆☆☆

Sound proofing ☆☆☆☆☆

Name: _____ Visiting from: _____

Date: _____ Time: _____ Duration: _____

Describe our bathroom in one word: _____

Do you scrunch or fold? Why? _____

Most memorable bathroom visited? _____

Best euphemism for performing #2? _____

Favorite bathroom activity: _____

Doodles & brilliant bathroom thoughts

During your visit did you

☐ Look in the medicine cabinet

☐ Check out your butt in the mirror

☐ Flush to cover up pooping sounds

☐ Reply to work emails / messages

☐ Scroll through social media

☐ Act to prevent any splashback

☐ Read through the entire guest book

Welcome To Our Bathroom

Name: _____ Visiting from: _____

Date: _____ Time: _____ Duration: _____

Describe our bathroom in one word: _____

Do you scrunch or fold? Why? _____

Most memorable bathroom visited? _____

Best euphemism for performing #2? _____

Favorite bathroom activity: _____

Rate your experience

Seat comfort ☆ ☆ ☆ ☆ ☆

Flush strength ☆ ☆ ☆ ☆ ☆

Ambience ☆ ☆ ☆ ☆ ☆

Paper quality ☆ ☆ ☆ ☆ ☆

Amenities ☆ ☆ ☆ ☆ ☆

Sound proofing ☆ ☆ ☆ ☆ ☆

During your visit did you

☐ Look in the medicine cabinet

☐ Check out your butt in the mirror

☐ Flush to cover up pooping sounds

☐ Reply to work emails / messages

☐ Scroll through social media

☐ Act to prevent any splashback

☐ Read through the entire guest book

Doodles & brilliant bathroom thoughts

Welcome To Our Bathroom

Rate your experience

Seat comfort ☆ ☆ ☆ ☆ ☆

Flush strength ☆ ☆ ☆ ☆ ☆

Ambience ☆ ☆ ☆ ☆ ☆

Paper quality ☆ ☆ ☆ ☆ ☆

Amenities ☆ ☆ ☆ ☆ ☆

Sound proofing ☆ ☆ ☆ ☆ ☆

Name: _____   Visiting from: _____

Date: _____   Time: _____   Duration: _____

Describe our bathroom in one word: _____

Do you scrunch or fold? Why? _____

Most memorable bathroom visited? _____

Best euphemism for performing #2? _____

Favorite bathroom activity: _____

Doodles & brilliant bathroom thoughts

During your visit did you

☐ Look in the medicine cabinet

☐ Check out your butt in the mirror

☐ Flush to cover up pooping sounds

☐ Reply to work emails / messages

☐ Scroll through social media

☐ Act to prevent any splashback

☐ Read through the entire guest book

Welcome To Our Bathroom

Name: Visiting from:

Date: Time: Duration:

Describe our bathroom in one word: _____

Do you scrunch or fold? Why? _____

Most memorable bathroom visited? _____

Best euphemism for performing #2? _____

Favorite bathroom activity: _____

Rate your experience

Seat comfort ☆ ☆ ☆ ☆ ☆

Flush strength ☆ ☆ ☆ ☆ ☆

Ambience ☆ ☆ ☆ ☆ ☆

Paper quality ☆ ☆ ☆ ☆ ☆

Amenities ☆ ☆ ☆ ☆ ☆

Sound proofing ☆ ☆ ☆ ☆ ☆

During your visit did you

☐ Look in the medicine cabinet

☐ Check out your butt in the mirror

☐ Flush to cover up pooping sounds

☐ Reply to work emails / messages

☐ Scroll through social media

☐ Act to prevent any splashback

☐ Read through the entire guest book

Doodles & brilliant bathroom thoughts

Welcome To Our Bathroom

Rate your experience

Seat comfort ☆ ☆ ☆ ☆ ☆

Flush strength ☆ ☆ ☆ ☆ ☆

Ambience ☆ ☆ ☆ ☆ ☆

Paper quality ☆ ☆ ☆ ☆ ☆

Amenities ☆ ☆ ☆ ☆ ☆

Sound proofing ☆ ☆ ☆ ☆ ☆

Name: _____ Visiting from: _____

Date: _____ Time: _____ Duration: _____

Describe our bathroom in one word: _____

Do you scrunch or fold? Why? _____

Most memorable bathroom visited? _____

Best euphemism for performing #2? _____

Favorite bathroom activity: _____

Doodles & brilliant bathroom thoughts

During your visit did you

☐ Look in the medicine cabinet

☐ Check out your butt in the mirror

☐ Flush to cover up pooping sounds

☐ Reply to work emails / messages

☐ Scroll through social media

☐ Act to prevent any splashback

☐ Read through the entire guest book

Welcome To Our Bathroom

Name:	Visiting from:	
Date:	Time:	Duration:

Describe our bathroom in one word: _____

Do you scrunch or fold? Why? _____

Most memorable bathroom visited? _____

Best euphemism for performing #2? _____

Favorite bathroom activity: _____

Rate your experience

Seat comfort	☆ ☆ ☆ ☆ ☆
Flush strength	☆ ☆ ☆ ☆ ☆
Ambience	☆ ☆ ☆ ☆ ☆
Paper quality	☆ ☆ ☆ ☆ ☆
Amenities	☆ ☆ ☆ ☆ ☆
Sound proofing	☆ ☆ ☆ ☆ ☆

During your visit did you

☐ Look in the medicine cabinet

☐ Check out your butt in the mirror

☐ Flush to cover up pooping sounds

☐ Reply to work emails / messages

☐ Scroll through social media

☐ Act to prevent any splashback

☐ Read through the entire guest book

Doodles & brilliant bathroom thoughts

Welcome To Our Bathroom

Rate your experience

Seat comfort ☆ ☆ ☆ ☆ ☆

Flush strength ☆ ☆ ☆ ☆ ☆

Ambience ☆ ☆ ☆ ☆ ☆

Paper quality ☆ ☆ ☆ ☆ ☆

Amenities ☆ ☆ ☆ ☆ ☆

Sound proofing ☆ ☆ ☆ ☆ ☆

Name: _____ Visiting from: _____

Date: _____ Time: _____ Duration: _____

Describe our bathroom in one word: _____

Do you scrunch or fold? Why? _____

Most memorable bathroom visited? _____

Best euphemism for performing #2? _____

Favorite bathroom activity: _____

Doodles & brilliant bathroom thoughts

During your visit did you

☐ Look in the medicine cabinet

☐ Check out your butt in the mirror

☐ Flush to cover up pooping sounds

☐ Reply to work emails / messages

☐ Scroll through social media

☐ Act to prevent any splashback

☐ Read through the entire guest book

Welcome To Our Bathroom

Name: _____ Visiting from: _____

Date: _____ Time: _____ Duration: _____

Describe our bathroom in one word: _____

Do you scrunch or fold? Why? _____

Most memorable bathroom visited? _____

Best euphemism for performing #2? _____

Favorite bathroom activity: _____

Rate your experience

Seat comfort ☆ ☆ ☆ ☆ ☆

Flush strength ☆ ☆ ☆ ☆ ☆

Ambience ☆ ☆ ☆ ☆ ☆

Paper quality ☆ ☆ ☆ ☆ ☆

Amenities ☆ ☆ ☆ ☆ ☆

Sound proofing ☆ ☆ ☆ ☆ ☆

During your visit did you

☐ Look in the medicine cabinet

☐ Check out your butt in the mirror

☐ Flush to cover up pooping sounds

☐ Reply to work emails / messages

☐ Scroll through social media

☐ Act to prevent any splashback

☐ Read through the entire guest book

Doodles & brilliant bathroom thoughts

Welcome To Our Bathroom

Rate your experience

Seat comfort ☆ ☆ ☆ ☆ ☆

Flush strength ☆ ☆ ☆ ☆ ☆

Ambience ☆ ☆ ☆ ☆ ☆

Paper quality ☆ ☆ ☆ ☆ ☆

Amenities ☆ ☆ ☆ ☆ ☆

Sound proofing ☆ ☆ ☆ ☆ ☆

Name: _____ Visiting from: _____

Date: _____ Time: _____ Duration: _____

Describe our bathroom in one word: _____

Do you scrunch or fold? Why? _____

Most memorable bathroom visited? _____

Best euphemism for performing #2? _____

Favorite bathroom activity: _____

Doodles & brilliant bathroom thoughts

During your visit did you

☐ Look in the medicine cabinet

☐ Check out your butt in the mirror

☐ Flush to cover up pooping sounds

☐ Reply to work emails / messages

☐ Scroll through social media

☐ Act to prevent any splashback

☐ Read through the entire guest book

Welcome To Our Bathroom

Name: _____ Visiting from: _____

Date: _____ Time: _____ Duration: _____

Describe our bathroom in one word: _____

Do you scrunch or fold? Why? _____

Most memorable bathroom visited? _____

Best euphemism for performing #2? _____

Favorite bathroom activity: _____

Rate your experience

Seat comfort	☆ ☆ ☆ ☆ ☆
Flush strength	☆ ☆ ☆ ☆ ☆
Ambience	☆ ☆ ☆ ☆ ☆
Paper quality	☆ ☆ ☆ ☆ ☆
Amenities	☆ ☆ ☆ ☆ ☆
Sound proofing	☆ ☆ ☆ ☆ ☆

During your visit did you

☐ Look in the medicine cabinet

☐ Check out your butt in the mirror

☐ Flush to cover up pooping sounds

☐ Reply to work emails / messages

☐ Scroll through social media

☐ Act to prevent any splashback

☐ Read through the entire guest book

Doodles & brilliant bathroom thoughts

Welcome To Our Bathroom

Rate your experience

Seat comfort ☆ ☆ ☆ ☆ ☆

Flush strength ☆ ☆ ☆ ☆ ☆

Ambience ☆ ☆ ☆ ☆ ☆

Paper quality ☆ ☆ ☆ ☆ ☆

Amenities ☆ ☆ ☆ ☆ ☆

Sound proofing ☆ ☆ ☆ ☆ ☆

Name: _____ Visiting from: _____

Date: _____ Time: _____ Duration: _____

Describe our bathroom in one word: _____

Do you scrunch or fold? Why? _____

Most memorable bathroom visited? _____

Best euphemism for performing #2? _____

Favorite bathroom activity: _____

Doodles & brilliant bathroom thoughts

During your visit did you

☐ Look in the medicine cabinet

☐ Check out your butt in the mirror

☐ Flush to cover up pooping sounds

☐ Reply to work emails / messages

☐ Scroll through social media

☐ Act to prevent any splashback

☐ Read through the entire guest book

Welcome To Our Bathroom

Name: _____ Visiting from: _____

Date: _____ Time: _____ Duration: _____

Describe our bathroom in one word: _____

Do you scrunch or fold? Why? _____

Most memorable bathroom visited? _____

Best euphemism for performing #2? _____

Favorite bathroom activity: _____

Rate your experience

Seat comfort ☆ ☆ ☆ ☆ ☆

Flush strength ☆ ☆ ☆ ☆ ☆

Ambience ☆ ☆ ☆ ☆ ☆

Paper quality ☆ ☆ ☆ ☆ ☆

Amenities ☆ ☆ ☆ ☆ ☆

Sound proofing ☆ ☆ ☆ ☆ ☆

During your visit did you

☐ Look in the medicine cabinet

☐ Check out your butt in the mirror

☐ Flush to cover up pooping sounds

☐ Reply to work emails / messages

☐ Scroll through social media

☐ Act to prevent any splashback

☐ Read through the entire guest book

Doodles & brilliant bathroom thoughts

Welcome To Our Bathroom

Rate your experience

Seat comfort ☆☆☆☆☆

Flush strength ☆☆☆☆☆

Ambience ☆☆☆☆☆

Paper quality ☆☆☆☆☆

Amenities ☆☆☆☆☆

Sound proofing ☆☆☆☆☆

Name: _____ Visiting from: _____

Date: _____ Time: _____ Duration: _____

Describe our bathroom in one word: _____

Do you scrunch or fold? Why? _____

Most memorable bathroom visited? _____

Best euphemism for performing #2? _____

Favorite bathroom activity: _____

Doodles & brilliant bathroom thoughts

During your visit did you

☐ Look in the medicine cabinet

☐ Check out your butt in the mirror

☐ Flush to cover up pooping sounds

☐ Reply to work emails / messages

☐ Scroll through social media

☐ Act to prevent any splashback

☐ Read through the entire guest book

Welcome To Our Bathroom

Name:	Visiting from:	
Date:	Time:	Duration:

Describe our bathroom in one word: _____

Do you scrunch or fold? Why? _____

Most memorable bathroom visited? _____

Best euphemism for performing #2? _____

Favorite bathroom activity: _____

Rate your experience

Seat comfort	☆ ☆ ☆ ☆ ☆
Flush strength	☆ ☆ ☆ ☆ ☆
Ambience	☆ ☆ ☆ ☆ ☆
Paper quality	☆ ☆ ☆ ☆ ☆
Amenities	☆ ☆ ☆ ☆ ☆
Sound proofing	☆ ☆ ☆ ☆ ☆

During your visit did you

☐ Look in the medicine cabinet

☐ Check out your butt in the mirror

☐ Flush to cover up pooping sounds

☐ Reply to work emails / messages

☐ Scroll through social media

☐ Act to prevent any splashback

☐ Read through the entire guest book

Doodles & brilliant bathroom thoughts

Welcome To Our Bathroom

Rate your experience

Seat comfort	☆ ☆ ☆ ☆ ☆
Flush strength	☆ ☆ ☆ ☆ ☆
Ambience	☆ ☆ ☆ ☆ ☆
Paper quality	☆ ☆ ☆ ☆ ☆
Amenities	☆ ☆ ☆ ☆ ☆
Sound proofing	☆ ☆ ☆ ☆ ☆

Name: _____   Visiting from: _____

Date: _____   Time: _____   Duration: _____

Describe our bathroom in one word: _____

Do you scrunch or fold? Why? _____

Most memorable bathroom visited? _____

Best euphemism for performing #2? _____

Favorite bathroom activity: _____

Doodles & brilliant bathroom thoughts

During your visit did you

☐ Look in the medicine cabinet

☐ Check out your butt in the mirror

☐ Flush to cover up pooping sounds

☐ Reply to work emails / messages

☐ Scroll through social media

☐ Act to prevent any splashback

☐ Read through the entire guest book

Welcome To Our Bathroom

Name: _____   Visiting from: _____

Date: _____   Time: _____   Duration: _____

Describe our bathroom in one word: _____

Do you scrunch or fold? Why? _____

Most memorable bathroom visited? _____

Best euphemism for performing #2? _____

Favorite bathroom activity: _____

Rate your experience

Seat comfort	☆ ☆ ☆ ☆ ☆
Flush strength	☆ ☆ ☆ ☆ ☆
Ambience	☆ ☆ ☆ ☆ ☆
Paper quality	☆ ☆ ☆ ☆ ☆
Amenities	☆ ☆ ☆ ☆ ☆
Sound proofing	☆ ☆ ☆ ☆ ☆

During your visit did you

☐ Look in the medicine cabinet

☐ Check out your butt in the mirror

☐ Flush to cover up pooping sounds

☐ Reply to work emails / messages

☐ Scroll through social media

☐ Act to prevent any splashback

☐ Read through the entire guest book

Doodles & brilliant bathroom thoughts

Welcome To Our Bathroom

Rate your experience

Seat comfort	☆ ☆ ☆ ☆ ☆
Flush strength	☆ ☆ ☆ ☆ ☆
Ambience	☆ ☆ ☆ ☆ ☆
Paper quality	☆ ☆ ☆ ☆ ☆
Amenities	☆ ☆ ☆ ☆ ☆
Sound proofing	☆ ☆ ☆ ☆ ☆

Name: _____   Visiting from: _____

Date: _____   Time: _____   Duration: _____

Describe our bathroom in one word: _____

Do you scrunch or fold? Why? _____

Most memorable bathroom visited? _____

Best euphemism for performing #2? _____

Favorite bathroom activity: _____

Doodles & brilliant bathroom thoughts

During your visit did you

☐ Look in the medicine cabinet

☐ Check out your butt in the mirror

☐ Flush to cover up pooping sounds

☐ Reply to work emails / messages

☐ Scroll through social media

☐ Act to prevent any splashback

☐ Read through the entire guest book

Welcome To Our Bathroom

Name: _____ Visiting from: _____

Date: _____ Time: _____ Duration: _____

Describe our bathroom in one word: _____

Do you scrunch or fold? Why? _____

Most memorable bathroom visited? _____

Best euphemism for performing #2? _____

Favorite bathroom activity: _____

Rate your experience

Seat comfort ☆ ☆ ☆ ☆ ☆

Flush strength ☆ ☆ ☆ ☆ ☆

Ambience ☆ ☆ ☆ ☆ ☆

Paper quality ☆ ☆ ☆ ☆ ☆

Amenities ☆ ☆ ☆ ☆ ☆

Sound proofing ☆ ☆ ☆ ☆ ☆

During your visit did you

☐ Look in the medicine cabinet

☐ Check out your butt in the mirror

☐ Flush to cover up pooping sounds

☐ Reply to work emails / messages

☐ Scroll through social media

☐ Act to prevent any splashback

☐ Read through the entire guest book

Doodles & brilliant bathroom thoughts

Welcome To Our Bathroom

Rate your experience

Seat comfort ☆☆☆☆☆

Flush strength ☆☆☆☆☆

Ambience ☆☆☆☆☆

Paper quality ☆☆☆☆☆

Amenities ☆☆☆☆☆

Sound proofing ☆☆☆☆☆

Name: _____ Visiting from: _____

Date: _____ Time: _____ Duration: _____

Describe our bathroom in one word: _____

Do you scrunch or fold? Why? _____

Most memorable bathroom visited? _____

Best euphemism for performing #2? _____

Favorite bathroom activity: _____

Doodles & brilliant bathroom thoughts

During your visit did you

☐ Look in the medicine cabinet

☐ Check out your butt in the mirror

☐ Flush to cover up pooping sounds

☐ Reply to work emails / messages

☐ Scroll through social media

☐ Act to prevent any splashback

☐ Read through the entire guest book

Welcome To Our Bathroom

Name: _____ Visiting from: _____

Date: _____ Time: _____ Duration: _____

Describe our bathroom in one word: _____

Do you scrunch or fold? Why? _____

Most memorable bathroom visited? _____

Best euphemism for performing #2? _____

Favorite bathroom activity: _____

Rate your experience

Seat comfort	☆ ☆ ☆ ☆ ☆
Flush strength	☆ ☆ ☆ ☆ ☆
Ambience	☆ ☆ ☆ ☆ ☆
Paper quality	☆ ☆ ☆ ☆ ☆
Amenities	☆ ☆ ☆ ☆ ☆
Sound proofing	☆ ☆ ☆ ☆ ☆

During your visit did you

☐ Look in the medicine cabinet

☐ Check out your butt in the mirror

☐ Flush to cover up pooping sounds

☐ Reply to work emails / messages

☐ Scroll through social media

☐ Act to prevent any splashback

☐ Read through the entire guest book

Doodles & brilliant bathroom thoughts

Welcome To Our Bathroom

Rate your experience

Seat comfort ☆☆☆☆☆

Flush strength ☆☆☆☆☆

Ambience ☆☆☆☆☆

Paper quality ☆☆☆☆☆

Amenities ☆☆☆☆☆

Sound proofing ☆☆☆☆☆

Name: _____ Visiting from: _____

Date: _____ Time: _____ Duration: _____

Describe our bathroom in one word: _____

Do you scrunch or fold? Why? _____

Most memorable bathroom visited? _____

Best euphemism for performing #2? _____

Favorite bathroom activity: _____

Doodles & brilliant bathroom thoughts

During your visit did you

☐ Look in the medicine cabinet

☐ Check out your butt in the mirror

☐ Flush to cover up pooping sounds

☐ Reply to work emails / messages

☐ Scroll through social media

☐ Act to prevent any splashback

☐ Read through the entire guest book

Welcome To Our Bathroom

Name: _____ Visiting from: _____

Date: _____ Time: _____ Duration: _____

Describe our bathroom in one word: _____

Do you scrunch or fold? Why? _____

Most memorable bathroom visited? _____

Best euphemism for performing #2? _____

Favorite bathroom activity: _____

Rate your experience

Seat comfort	☆ ☆ ☆ ☆ ☆
Flush strength	☆ ☆ ☆ ☆ ☆
Ambience	☆ ☆ ☆ ☆ ☆
Paper quality	☆ ☆ ☆ ☆ ☆
Amenities	☆ ☆ ☆ ☆ ☆
Sound proofing	☆ ☆ ☆ ☆ ☆

During your visit did you

☐ Look in the medicine cabinet

☐ Check out your butt in the mirror

☐ Flush to cover up pooping sounds

☐ Reply to work emails / messages

☐ Scroll through social media

☐ Act to prevent any splashback

☐ Read through the entire guest book

Doodles & brilliant bathroom thoughts

Welcome To Our Bathroom

Rate your experience

Seat comfort	☆☆☆☆☆
Flush strength	☆☆☆☆☆
Ambience	☆☆☆☆☆
Paper quality	☆☆☆☆☆
Amenities	☆☆☆☆☆
Sound proofing	☆☆☆☆☆

Name: _____ Visiting from: _____

Date: _____ Time: _____ Duration: _____

Describe our bathroom in one word: _____

Do you scrunch or fold? Why? _____

Most memorable bathroom visited? _____

Best euphemism for performing #2? _____

Favorite bathroom activity: _____

Doodles & brilliant bathroom thoughts

During your visit did you

☐ Look in the medicine cabinet

☐ Check out your butt in the mirror

☐ Flush to cover up pooping sounds

☐ Reply to work emails / messages

☐ Scroll through social media

☐ Act to prevent any splashback

☐ Read through the entire guest book

Welcome To Our Bathroom

Name: _____ Visiting from: _____

Date: _____ Time: _____ Duration: _____

Describe our bathroom in one word: _____

Do you scrunch or fold? Why? _____

Most memorable bathroom visited? _____

Best euphemism for performing #2? _____

Favorite bathroom activity: _____

Rate your experience

Seat comfort	☆	☆	☆	☆	☆
Flush strength	☆	☆	☆	☆	☆
Ambience	☆	☆	☆	☆	☆
Paper quality	☆	☆	☆	☆	☆
Amenities	☆	☆	☆	☆	☆
Sound proofing	☆	☆	☆	☆	☆

During your visit did you

☐ Look in the medicine cabinet

☐ Check out your butt in the mirror

☐ Flush to cover up pooping sounds

☐ Reply to work emails / messages

☐ Scroll through social media

☐ Act to prevent any splashback

☐ Read through the entire guest book

Doodles & brilliant bathroom thoughts

Welcome To Our Bathroom

Rate your experience

Seat comfort ☆ ☆ ☆ ☆ ☆

Flush strength ☆ ☆ ☆ ☆ ☆

Ambience ☆ ☆ ☆ ☆ ☆

Paper quality ☆ ☆ ☆ ☆ ☆

Amenities ☆ ☆ ☆ ☆ ☆

Sound proofing ☆ ☆ ☆ ☆ ☆

Name: _____ Visiting from: _____

Date: _____ Time: _____ Duration: _____

Describe our bathroom in one word: _____

Do you scrunch or fold? Why? _____

Most memorable bathroom visited? _____

Best euphemism for performing #2? _____

Favorite bathroom activity: _____

Doodles & brilliant bathroom thoughts

During your visit did you

☐ Look in the medicine cabinet

☐ Check out your butt in the mirror

☐ Flush to cover up pooping sounds

☐ Reply to work emails / messages

☐ Scroll through social media

☐ Act to prevent any splashback

☐ Read through the entire guest book

Welcome To Our Bathroom

Name: _____   Visiting from: _____

Date: _____   Time: _____   Duration: _____

Describe our bathroom in one word: _____

Do you scrunch or fold? Why? _____

Most memorable bathroom visited? _____

Best euphemism for performing #2? _____

Favorite bathroom activity: _____

Rate your experience

Seat comfort   ☆ ☆ ☆ ☆ ☆

Flush strength   ☆ ☆ ☆ ☆ ☆

Ambience   ☆ ☆ ☆ ☆ ☆

Paper quality   ☆ ☆ ☆ ☆ ☆

Amenities   ☆ ☆ ☆ ☆ ☆

Sound proofing ☆ ☆ ☆ ☆ ☆

During your visit did you

☐ Look in the medicine cabinet

☐ Check out your butt in the mirror

☐ Flush to cover up pooping sounds

☐ Reply to work emails / messages

☐ Scroll through social media

☐ Act to prevent any splashback

☐ Read through the entire guest book

Doodles & brilliant bathroom thoughts

Welcome To Our Bathroom

Rate your experience

Seat comfort ☆☆☆☆☆

Flush strength ☆☆☆☆☆

Ambience ☆☆☆☆☆

Paper quality ☆☆☆☆☆

Amenities ☆☆☆☆☆

Sound proofing ☆☆☆☆☆

Name: _____   Visiting from: _____

Date: _____   Time: _____   Duration: _____

Describe our bathroom in one word: _____

Do you scrunch or fold? Why? _____

Most memorable bathroom visited? _____

Best euphemism for performing #2? _____

Favorite bathroom activity: _____

Doodles & brilliant bathroom thoughts

During your visit did you

☐ Look in the medicine cabinet

☐ Check out your butt in the mirror

☐ Flush to cover up pooping sounds

☐ Reply to work emails / messages

☐ Scroll through social media

☐ Act to prevent any splashback

☐ Read through the entire guest book

Welcome To Our Bathroom

Name: _____ Visiting from: _____

Date: _____ Time: _____ Duration: _____

Describe our bathroom in one word: _____

Do you scrunch or fold? Why? _____

Most memorable bathroom visited? _____

Best euphemism for performing #2? _____

Favorite bathroom activity: _____

Rate your experience

Seat comfort	☆ ☆ ☆ ☆ ☆
Flush strength	☆ ☆ ☆ ☆ ☆
Ambience	☆ ☆ ☆ ☆ ☆
Paper quality	☆ ☆ ☆ ☆ ☆
Amenities	☆ ☆ ☆ ☆ ☆
Sound proofing	☆ ☆ ☆ ☆ ☆

During your visit did you

☐ Look in the medicine cabinet

☐ Check out your butt in the mirror

☐ Flush to cover up pooping sounds

☐ Reply to work emails / messages

☐ Scroll through social media

☐ Act to prevent any splashback

☐ Read through the entire guest book

Doodles & brilliant bathroom thoughts

Welcome To Our Bathroom

Rate your experience

Seat comfort ☆ ☆ ☆ ☆ ☆

Flush strength ☆ ☆ ☆ ☆ ☆

Ambience ☆ ☆ ☆ ☆ ☆

Paper quality ☆ ☆ ☆ ☆ ☆

Amenities ☆ ☆ ☆ ☆ ☆

Sound proofing ☆ ☆ ☆ ☆ ☆

Name: _____   Visiting from: _____

Date: _____   Time: _____   Duration: _____

Describe our bathroom in one word: _____

Do you scrunch or fold? Why? _____

Most memorable bathroom visited? _____

Best euphemism for performing #2? _____

Favorite bathroom activity: _____

Doodles & brilliant bathroom thoughts

During your visit did you

☐ Look in the medicine cabinet

☐ Check out your butt in the mirror

☐ Flush to cover up pooping sounds

☐ Reply to work emails / messages

☐ Scroll through social media

☐ Act to prevent any splashback

☐ Read through the entire guest book

Welcome To Our Bathroom

Name: Visiting from:

Date: Time: Duration:

Describe our bathroom in one word: _____

Do you scrunch or fold? Why? _____

Most memorable bathroom visited? _____

Best euphemism for performing #2? _____

Favorite bathroom activity: _____

Rate your experience

Seat comfort   ☆ ☆ ☆ ☆ ☆

Flush strength   ☆ ☆ ☆ ☆ ☆

Ambience   ☆ ☆ ☆ ☆ ☆

Paper quality   ☆ ☆ ☆ ☆ ☆

Amenities   ☆ ☆ ☆ ☆ ☆

Sound proofing ☆ ☆ ☆ ☆ ☆

During your visit did you

☐ Look in the medicine cabinet

☐ Check out your butt in the mirror

☐ Flush to cover up pooping sounds

☐ Reply to work emails / messages

☐ Scroll through social media

☐ Act to prevent any splashback

☐ Read through the entire guest book

Doodles & brilliant bathroom thoughts

Welcome To Our Bathroom

Rate your experience

Seat comfort ☆☆☆☆☆

Flush strength ☆☆☆☆☆

Ambience ☆☆☆☆☆

Paper quality ☆☆☆☆☆

Amenities ☆☆☆☆☆

Sound proofing ☆☆☆☆☆

Name: _____ Visiting from: _____

Date: _____ Time: _____ Duration: _____

Describe our bathroom in one word: _____

Do you scrunch or fold? Why? _____

Most memorable bathroom visited? _____

Best euphemism for performing #2? _____

Favorite bathroom activity: _____

Doodles & brilliant bathroom thoughts

During your visit did you

☐ Look in the medicine cabinet

☐ Check out your butt in the mirror

☐ Flush to cover up pooping sounds

☐ Reply to work emails / messages

☐ Scroll through social media

☐ Act to prevent any splashback

☐ Read through the entire guest book

Welcome To Our Bathroom

Name: _____ Visiting from: _____

Date: _____ Time: _____ Duration: _____

Describe our bathroom in one word: _____

Do you scrunch or fold? Why? _____

Most memorable bathroom visited? _____

Best euphemism for performing #2? _____

Favorite bathroom activity: _____

Rate your experience

Seat comfort ☆ ☆ ☆ ☆ ☆

Flush strength ☆ ☆ ☆ ☆ ☆

Ambience ☆ ☆ ☆ ☆ ☆

Paper quality ☆ ☆ ☆ ☆ ☆

Amenities ☆ ☆ ☆ ☆ ☆

Sound proofing ☆ ☆ ☆ ☆ ☆

During your visit did you

☐ Look in the medicine cabinet

☐ Check out your butt in the mirror

☐ Flush to cover up pooping sounds

☐ Reply to work emails / messages

☐ Scroll through social media

☐ Act to prevent any splashback

☐ Read through the entire guest book

Doodles & brilliant bathroom thoughts

Welcome To Our Bathroom

Rate your experience

Seat comfort ☆ ☆ ☆ ☆ ☆

Flush strength ☆ ☆ ☆ ☆ ☆

Ambience ☆ ☆ ☆ ☆ ☆

Paper quality ☆ ☆ ☆ ☆ ☆

Amenities ☆ ☆ ☆ ☆ ☆

Sound proofing ☆ ☆ ☆ ☆ ☆

Name: _____ Visiting from: _____

Date: _____ Time: _____ Duration: _____

Describe our bathroom in one word: _____

Do you scrunch or fold? Why? _____

Most memorable bathroom visited? _____

Best euphemism for performing #2? _____

Favorite bathroom activity: _____

Doodles & brilliant bathroom thoughts

During your visit did you

☐ Look in the medicine cabinet

☐ Check out your butt in the mirror

☐ Flush to cover up pooping sounds

☐ Reply to work emails / messages

☐ Scroll through social media

☐ Act to prevent any splashback

☐ Read through the entire guest book

Welcome To Our Bathroom

Name: _____   Visiting from: _____

Date: _____   Time: _____   Duration: _____

Describe our bathroom in one word: _____

Do you scrunch or fold? Why? _____

Most memorable bathroom visited? _____

Best euphemism for performing #2? _____

Favorite bathroom activity: _____

Rate your experience

Seat comfort ☆ ☆ ☆ ☆ ☆

Flush strength ☆ ☆ ☆ ☆ ☆

Ambience ☆ ☆ ☆ ☆ ☆

Paper quality ☆ ☆ ☆ ☆ ☆

Amenities ☆ ☆ ☆ ☆ ☆

Sound proofing ☆ ☆ ☆ ☆ ☆

During your visit did you

☐ Look in the medicine cabinet

☐ Check out your butt in the mirror

☐ Flush to cover up pooping sounds

☐ Reply to work emails / messages

☐ Scroll through social media

☐ Act to prevent any splashback

☐ Read through the entire guest book

Doodles & brilliant bathroom thoughts

Welcome To Our Bathroom

Rate your experience

Seat comfort ☆ ☆ ☆ ☆ ☆

Flush strength ☆ ☆ ☆ ☆ ☆

Ambience ☆ ☆ ☆ ☆ ☆

Paper quality ☆ ☆ ☆ ☆ ☆

Amenities ☆ ☆ ☆ ☆ ☆

Sound proofing ☆ ☆ ☆ ☆ ☆

Name: _____   Visiting from: _____

Date: _____   Time: _____   Duration: _____

Describe our bathroom in one word: _____

Do you scrunch or fold? Why? _____

Most memorable bathroom visited? _____

Best euphemism for performing #2? _____

Favorite bathroom activity: _____

Doodles & brilliant bathroom thoughts

During your visit did you

☐ Look in the medicine cabinet

☐ Check out your butt in the mirror

☐ Flush to cover up pooping sounds

☐ Reply to work emails / messages

☐ Scroll through social media

☐ Act to prevent any splashback

☐ Read through the entire guest book

Welcome To Our Bathroom

Name: _____ Visiting from: _____

Date: _____ Time: _____ Duration: _____

Describe our bathroom in one word: _____

Do you scrunch or fold? Why? _____

Most memorable bathroom visited? _____

Best euphemism for performing #2? _____

Favorite bathroom activity: _____

Rate your experience

Seat comfort ☆ ☆ ☆ ☆ ☆

Flush strength ☆ ☆ ☆ ☆ ☆

Ambience ☆ ☆ ☆ ☆ ☆

Paper quality ☆ ☆ ☆ ☆ ☆

Amenities ☆ ☆ ☆ ☆ ☆

Sound proofing ☆ ☆ ☆ ☆ ☆

During your visit did you

☐ Look in the medicine cabinet

☐ Check out your butt in the mirror

☐ Flush to cover up pooping sounds

☐ Reply to work emails / messages

☐ Scroll through social media

☐ Act to prevent any splashback

☐ Read through the entire guest book

Doodles & brilliant bathroom thoughts

Welcome To Our Bathroom

Rate your experience

Seat comfort	☆ ☆ ☆ ☆ ☆
Flush strength	☆ ☆ ☆ ☆ ☆
Ambience	☆ ☆ ☆ ☆ ☆
Paper quality	☆ ☆ ☆ ☆ ☆
Amenities	☆ ☆ ☆ ☆ ☆
Sound proofing	☆ ☆ ☆ ☆ ☆

Name: _____ Visiting from: _____

Date: _____ Time: _____ Duration: _____

Describe our bathroom in one word: _____

Do you scrunch or fold? Why? _____

Most memorable bathroom visited? _____

Best euphemism for performing #2? _____

Favorite bathroom activity: _____

Doodles & brilliant bathroom thoughts

During your visit did you

☐ Look in the medicine cabinet

☐ Check out your butt in the mirror

☐ Flush to cover up pooping sounds

☐ Reply to work emails / messages

☐ Scroll through social media

☐ Act to prevent any splashback

☐ Read through the entire guest book

Welcome To Our Bathroom

Name: _____   Visiting from: _____

Date: _____   Time: _____   Duration: _____

Describe our bathroom in one word: _____

Do you scrunch or fold? Why? _____

Most memorable bathroom visited? _____

Best euphemism for performing #2? _____

Favorite bathroom activity: _____

Rate your experience

Seat comfort ☆ ☆ ☆ ☆ ☆

Flush strength ☆ ☆ ☆ ☆ ☆

Ambience ☆ ☆ ☆ ☆ ☆

Paper quality ☆ ☆ ☆ ☆ ☆

Amenities ☆ ☆ ☆ ☆ ☆

Sound proofing ☆ ☆ ☆ ☆ ☆

During your visit did you

☐ Look in the medicine cabinet

☐ Check out your butt in the mirror

☐ Flush to cover up pooping sounds

☐ Reply to work emails / messages

☐ Scroll through social media

☐ Act to prevent any splashback

☐ Read through the entire guest book

Doodles & brilliant bathroom thoughts

Welcome To Our Bathroom

Rate your experience

Seat comfort ☆ ☆ ☆ ☆ ☆

Flush strength ☆ ☆ ☆ ☆ ☆

Ambience ☆ ☆ ☆ ☆ ☆

Paper quality ☆ ☆ ☆ ☆ ☆

Amenities ☆ ☆ ☆ ☆ ☆

Sound proofing ☆ ☆ ☆ ☆ ☆

Name: _____ Visiting from: _____

Date: _____ Time: _____ Duration: _____

Describe our bathroom in one word: _____

Do you scrunch or fold? Why? _____

Most memorable bathroom visited? _____

Best euphemism for performing #2? _____

Favorite bathroom activity: _____

Doodles & brilliant bathroom thoughts

During your visit did you

☐ Look in the medicine cabinet

☐ Check out your butt in the mirror

☐ Flush to cover up pooping sounds

☐ Reply to work emails / messages

☐ Scroll through social media

☐ Act to prevent any splashback

☐ Read through the entire guest book

Welcome To Our Bathroom

Name: _____ Visiting from: _____

Date: _____ Time: _____ Duration: _____

Describe our bathroom in one word: _____

Do you scrunch or fold? Why? _____

Most memorable bathroom visited? _____

Best euphemism for performing #2? _____

Favorite bathroom activity: _____

Rate your experience

Seat comfort	☆ ☆ ☆ ☆ ☆
Flush strength	☆ ☆ ☆ ☆ ☆
Ambience	☆ ☆ ☆ ☆ ☆
Paper quality	☆ ☆ ☆ ☆ ☆
Amenities	☆ ☆ ☆ ☆ ☆
Sound proofing	☆ ☆ ☆ ☆ ☆

During your visit did you

☐ Look in the medicine cabinet

☐ Check out your butt in the mirror

☐ Flush to cover up pooping sounds

☐ Reply to work emails / messages

☐ Scroll through social media

☐ Act to prevent any splashback

☐ Read through the entire guest book

Doodles & brilliant bathroom thoughts

Welcome To Our Bathroom

Rate your experience

Seat comfort ☆☆☆☆☆

Flush strength ☆☆☆☆☆

Ambience ☆☆☆☆☆

Paper quality ☆☆☆☆☆

Amenities ☆☆☆☆☆

Sound proofing ☆☆☆☆☆

Name: _____ Visiting from: _____

Date: _____ Time: _____ Duration: _____

Describe our bathroom in one word: _____

Do you scrunch or fold? Why? _____

Most memorable bathroom visited? _____

Best euphemism for performing #2? _____

Favorite bathroom activity: _____

Doodles & brilliant bathroom thoughts

During your visit did you

☐ Look in the medicine cabinet

☐ Check out your butt in the mirror

☐ Flush to cover up pooping sounds

☐ Reply to work emails / messages

☐ Scroll through social media

☐ Act to prevent any splashback

☐ Read through the entire guest book

Welcome To Our Bathroom

Name: _____ Visiting from: _____

Date: _____ Time: _____ Duration: _____

Describe our bathroom in one word: _____

Do you scrunch or fold? Why? _____

Most memorable bathroom visited? _____

Best euphemism for performing #2? _____

Favorite bathroom activity: _____

Rate your experience

Seat comfort ☆ ☆ ☆ ☆ ☆

Flush strength ☆ ☆ ☆ ☆ ☆

Ambience ☆ ☆ ☆ ☆ ☆

Paper quality ☆ ☆ ☆ ☆ ☆

Amenities ☆ ☆ ☆ ☆ ☆

Sound proofing ☆ ☆ ☆ ☆ ☆

During your visit did you

☐ Look in the medicine cabinet

☐ Check out your butt in the mirror

☐ Flush to cover up pooping sounds

☐ Reply to work emails / messages

☐ Scroll through social media

☐ Act to prevent any splashback

☐ Read through the entire guest book

Doodles & brilliant bathroom thoughts

Welcome To Our Bathroom

Rate your experience

Seat comfort ☆ ☆ ☆ ☆ ☆

Flush strength ☆ ☆ ☆ ☆ ☆

Ambience ☆ ☆ ☆ ☆ ☆

Paper quality ☆ ☆ ☆ ☆ ☆

Amenities ☆ ☆ ☆ ☆ ☆

Sound proofing ☆ ☆ ☆ ☆ ☆

Name: _____ Visiting from: _____

Date: _____ Time: _____ Duration: _____

Describe our bathroom in one word: _____

Do you scrunch or fold? Why? _____

Most memorable bathroom visited? _____

Best euphemism for performing #2? _____

Favorite bathroom activity: _____

Doodles & brilliant bathroom thoughts

During your visit did you

☐ Look in the medicine cabinet

☐ Check out your butt in the mirror

☐ Flush to cover up pooping sounds

☐ Reply to work emails / messages

☐ Scroll through social media

☐ Act to prevent any splashback

☐ Read through the entire guest book

Welcome To Our Bathroom

Name: _____ Visiting from: _____

Date: _____ Time: _____ Duration: _____

Describe our bathroom in one word: _____

Do you scrunch or fold? Why? _____

Most memorable bathroom visited? _____

Best euphemism for performing #2? _____

Favorite bathroom activity: _____

Rate your experience

Seat comfort	☆ ☆ ☆ ☆ ☆
Flush strength	☆ ☆ ☆ ☆ ☆
Ambience	☆ ☆ ☆ ☆ ☆
Paper quality	☆ ☆ ☆ ☆ ☆
Amenities	☆ ☆ ☆ ☆ ☆
Sound proofing	☆ ☆ ☆ ☆ ☆

During your visit did you

☐ Look in the medicine cabinet

☐ Check out your butt in the mirror

☐ Flush to cover up pooping sounds

☐ Reply to work emails / messages

☐ Scroll through social media

☐ Act to prevent any splashback

☐ Read through the entire guest book

Doodles & brilliant bathroom thoughts

Welcome To Our Bathroom

Rate your experience

Seat comfort ☆☆☆☆☆

Flush strength ☆☆☆☆☆

Ambience ☆☆☆☆☆

Paper quality ☆☆☆☆☆

Amenities ☆☆☆☆☆

Sound proofing ☆☆☆☆☆

Name: _____   Visiting from: _____

Date: _____   Time: _____   Duration: _____

Describe our bathroom in one word: _____

Do you scrunch or fold? Why? _____

Most memorable bathroom visited? _____

Best euphemism for performing #2? _____

Favorite bathroom activity: _____

Doodles & brilliant bathroom thoughts

During your visit did you

☐ Look in the medicine cabinet

☐ Check out your butt in the mirror

☐ Flush to cover up pooping sounds

☐ Reply to work emails / messages

☐ Scroll through social media

☐ Act to prevent any splashback

☐ Read through the entire guest book

Welcome To Our Bathroom

Name: _____   Visiting from: _____

Date: _____   Time: _____   Duration: _____

Describe our bathroom in one word: _____

Do you scrunch or fold? Why? _____

Most memorable bathroom visited? _____

Best euphemism for performing #2? _____

Favorite bathroom activity: _____

Rate your experience

Seat comfort ☆ ☆ ☆ ☆ ☆

Flush strength ☆ ☆ ☆ ☆ ☆

Ambience ☆ ☆ ☆ ☆ ☆

Paper quality ☆ ☆ ☆ ☆ ☆

Amenities ☆ ☆ ☆ ☆ ☆

Sound proofing ☆ ☆ ☆ ☆ ☆

During your visit did you

☐ Look in the medicine cabinet

☐ Check out your butt in the mirror

☐ Flush to cover up pooping sounds

☐ Reply to work emails / messages

☐ Scroll through social media

☐ Act to prevent any splashback

☐ Read through the entire guest book

Doodles & brilliant bathroom thoughts

Welcome To Our Bathroom

Rate your experience

Seat comfort ☆ ☆ ☆ ☆ ☆

Flush strength ☆ ☆ ☆ ☆ ☆

Ambience ☆ ☆ ☆ ☆ ☆

Paper quality ☆ ☆ ☆ ☆ ☆

Amenities ☆ ☆ ☆ ☆ ☆

Sound proofing ☆ ☆ ☆ ☆ ☆

Name: _____ Visiting from: _____

Date: _____ Time: _____ Duration: _____

Describe our bathroom in one word: _____

Do you scrunch or fold? Why? _____

Most memorable bathroom visited? _____

Best euphemism for performing #2? _____

Favorite bathroom activity: _____

Doodles & brilliant bathroom thoughts

During your visit did you

☐ Look in the medicine cabinet

☐ Check out your butt in the mirror

☐ Flush to cover up pooping sounds

☐ Reply to work emails / messages

☐ Scroll through social media

☐ Act to prevent any splashback

☐ Read through the entire guest book

Welcome To Our Bathroom

Name: _____   Visiting from: _____

Date: _____   Time: _____   Duration: _____

Describe our bathroom in one word: _____

Do you scrunch or fold? Why? _____

Most memorable bathroom visited? _____

Best euphemism for performing #2? _____

Favorite bathroom activity: _____

Rate your experience

Seat comfort	☆ ☆ ☆ ☆ ☆
Flush strength	☆ ☆ ☆ ☆ ☆
Ambience	☆ ☆ ☆ ☆ ☆
Paper quality	☆ ☆ ☆ ☆ ☆
Amenities	☆ ☆ ☆ ☆ ☆
Sound proofing	☆ ☆ ☆ ☆ ☆

During your visit did you

☐ Look in the medicine cabinet

☐ Check out your butt in the mirror

☐ Flush to cover up pooping sounds

☐ Reply to work emails / messages

☐ Scroll through social media

☐ Act to prevent any splashback

☐ Read through the entire guest book

Doodles & brilliant bathroom thoughts

Welcome To Our Bathroom

Rate your experience

Seat comfort ☆☆☆☆☆

Flush strength ☆☆☆☆☆

Ambience ☆☆☆☆☆

Paper quality ☆☆☆☆☆

Amenities ☆☆☆☆☆

Sound proofing ☆☆☆☆☆

Name: _____ Visiting from: _____

Date: _____ Time: _____ Duration: _____

Describe our bathroom in one word: _____

Do you scrunch or fold? Why? _____

Most memorable bathroom visited? _____

Best euphemism for performing #2? _____

Favorite bathroom activity: _____

Doodles & brilliant bathroom thoughts

During your visit did you

☐ Look in the medicine cabinet

☐ Check out your butt in the mirror

☐ Flush to cover up pooping sounds

☐ Reply to work emails / messages

☐ Scroll through social media

☐ Act to prevent any splashback

☐ Read through the entire guest book

Welcome To Our Bathroom

Name: _____ Visiting from: _____

Date: _____ Time: _____ Duration: _____

Describe our bathroom in one word: _____

Do you scrunch or fold? Why? _____

Most memorable bathroom visited? _____

Best euphemism for performing #2? _____

Favorite bathroom activity: _____

Rate your experience

Seat comfort	☆ ☆ ☆ ☆ ☆	
Flush strength	☆ ☆ ☆ ☆ ☆	
Ambience	☆ ☆ ☆ ☆ ☆	
Paper quality	☆ ☆ ☆ ☆ ☆	
Amenities	☆ ☆ ☆ ☆ ☆	
Sound proofing	☆ ☆ ☆ ☆ ☆	

During your visit did you

- ☐ Look in the medicine cabinet
- ☐ Check out your butt in the mirror
- ☐ Flush to cover up pooping sounds
- ☐ Reply to work emails / messages
- ☐ Scroll through social media
- ☐ Act to prevent any splashback
- ☐ Read through the entire guest book

Doodles & brilliant bathroom thoughts

Welcome To Our Bathroom

Rate your experience

Seat comfort ☆☆☆☆☆

Flush strength ☆☆☆☆☆

Ambience ☆☆☆☆☆

Paper quality ☆☆☆☆☆

Amenities ☆☆☆☆☆

Sound proofing ☆☆☆☆☆

Name: _____   Visiting from: _____

Date: _____   Time: _____   Duration: _____

Describe our bathroom in one word: _____

Do you scrunch or fold? Why? _____

Most memorable bathroom visited? _____

Best euphemism for performing #2? _____

Favorite bathroom activity: _____

Doodles & brilliant bathroom thoughts

During your visit did you

☐ Look in the medicine cabinet

☐ Check out your butt in the mirror

☐ Flush to cover up pooping sounds

☐ Reply to work emails / messages

☐ Scroll through social media

☐ Act to prevent any splashback

☐ Read through the entire guest book

Welcome To Our Bathroom

Name: _____ Visiting from: _____

Date: _____ Time: _____ Duration: _____

Describe our bathroom in one word: _____

Do you scrunch or fold? Why? _____

Most memorable bathroom visited? _____

Best euphemism for performing #2? _____

Favorite bathroom activity: _____

Rate your experience

Seat comfort	☆ ☆ ☆ ☆ ☆
Flush strength	☆ ☆ ☆ ☆ ☆
Ambience	☆ ☆ ☆ ☆ ☆
Paper quality	☆ ☆ ☆ ☆ ☆
Amenities	☆ ☆ ☆ ☆ ☆
Sound proofing	☆ ☆ ☆ ☆ ☆

During your visit did you

☐ Look in the medicine cabinet

☐ Check out your butt in the mirror

☐ Flush to cover up pooping sounds

☐ Reply to work emails / messages

☐ Scroll through social media

☐ Act to prevent any splashback

☐ Read through the entire guest book

Doodles & brilliant bathroom thoughts

Welcome To Our Bathroom

Rate your experience

Seat comfort ☆☆☆☆☆

Flush strength ☆☆☆☆☆

Ambience ☆☆☆☆☆

Paper quality ☆☆☆☆☆

Amenities ☆☆☆☆☆

Sound proofing ☆☆☆☆☆

Name: _____ Visiting from: _____

Date: _____ Time: _____ Duration: _____

Describe our bathroom in one word: _____

Do you scrunch or fold? Why? _____

Most memorable bathroom visited? _____

Best euphemism for performing #2? _____

Favorite bathroom activity: _____

Doodles & brilliant bathroom thoughts

During your visit did you

☐ Look in the medicine cabinet

☐ Check out your butt in the mirror

☐ Flush to cover up pooping sounds

☐ Reply to work emails / messages

☐ Scroll through social media

☐ Act to prevent any splashback

☐ Read through the entire guest book

Welcome To Our Bathroom

Name: _____ Visiting from: _____

Date: _____ Time: _____ Duration: _____

Describe our bathroom in one word: _____

Do you scrunch or fold? Why? _____

Most memorable bathroom visited? _____

Best euphemism for performing #2? _____

Favorite bathroom activity: _____

Rate your experience

Seat comfort ☆ ☆ ☆ ☆ ☆

Flush strength ☆ ☆ ☆ ☆ ☆

Ambience ☆ ☆ ☆ ☆ ☆

Paper quality ☆ ☆ ☆ ☆ ☆

Amenities ☆ ☆ ☆ ☆ ☆

Sound proofing ☆ ☆ ☆ ☆ ☆

During your visit did you

☐ Look in the medicine cabinet

☐ Check out your butt in the mirror

☐ Flush to cover up pooping sounds

☐ Reply to work emails / messages

☐ Scroll through social media

☐ Act to prevent any splashback

☐ Read through the entire guest book

Doodles & brilliant bathroom thoughts

Welcome To Our Bathroom

Rate your experience

Seat comfort ☆ ☆ ☆ ☆ ☆

Flush strength ☆ ☆ ☆ ☆ ☆

Ambience ☆ ☆ ☆ ☆ ☆

Paper quality ☆ ☆ ☆ ☆ ☆

Amenities ☆ ☆ ☆ ☆ ☆

Sound proofing ☆ ☆ ☆ ☆ ☆

Name: _____ Visiting from: _____

Date: _____ Time: _____ Duration: _____

Describe our bathroom in one word: _____

Do you scrunch or fold? Why? _____

Most memorable bathroom visited? _____

Best euphemism for performing #2? _____

Favorite bathroom activity: _____

Doodles & brilliant bathroom thoughts

During your visit did you

☐ Look in the medicine cabinet

☐ Check out your butt in the mirror

☐ Flush to cover up pooping sounds

☐ Reply to work emails / messages

☐ Scroll through social media

☐ Act to prevent any splashback

☐ Read through the entire guest book

Welcome To Our Bathroom

Name: _____ Visiting from: _____

Date: _____ Time: _____ Duration: _____

Describe our bathroom in one word: _____

Do you scrunch or fold? Why? _____

Most memorable bathroom visited? _____

Best euphemism for performing #2? _____

Favorite bathroom activity: _____

Rate your experience

Seat comfort	☆ ☆ ☆ ☆ ☆
Flush strength	☆ ☆ ☆ ☆ ☆
Ambience	☆ ☆ ☆ ☆ ☆
Paper quality	☆ ☆ ☆ ☆ ☆
Amenities	☆ ☆ ☆ ☆ ☆
Sound proofing	☆ ☆ ☆ ☆ ☆

During your visit did you

☐ Look in the medicine cabinet

☐ Check out your butt in the mirror

☐ Flush to cover up pooping sounds

☐ Reply to work emails / messages

☐ Scroll through social media

☐ Act to prevent any splashback

☐ Read through the entire guest book

Doodles & brilliant bathroom thoughts

Welcome To Our Bathroom

Rate your experience

Seat comfort ☆ ☆ ☆ ☆ ☆

Flush strength ☆ ☆ ☆ ☆ ☆

Ambience ☆ ☆ ☆ ☆ ☆

Paper quality ☆ ☆ ☆ ☆ ☆

Amenities ☆ ☆ ☆ ☆ ☆

Sound proofing ☆ ☆ ☆ ☆ ☆

Name: _____   Visiting from: _____

Date: _____   Time: _____   Duration: _____

Describe our bathroom in one word: _____

Do you scrunch or fold? Why? _____

Most memorable bathroom visited? _____

Best euphemism for performing #2? _____

Favorite bathroom activity: _____

Doodles & brilliant bathroom thoughts

During your visit did you

☐ Look in the medicine cabinet

☐ Check out your butt in the mirror

☐ Flush to cover up pooping sounds

☐ Reply to work emails / messages

☐ Scroll through social media

☐ Act to prevent any splashback

☐ Read through the entire guest book

Welcome To Our Bathroom

Name: _____ Visiting from: _____

Date: _____ Time: _____ Duration: _____

Describe our bathroom in one word: _____

Do you scrunch or fold? Why? _____

Most memorable bathroom visited? _____

Best euphemism for performing #2? _____

Favorite bathroom activity: _____

Rate your experience

Seat comfort	☆	☆	☆	☆	☆
Flush strength	☆	☆	☆	☆	☆
Ambience	☆	☆	☆	☆	☆
Paper quality	☆	☆	☆	☆	☆
Amenities	☆	☆	☆	☆	☆
Sound proofing	☆	☆	☆	☆	☆

During your visit did you

☐ Look in the medicine cabinet

☐ Check out your butt in the mirror

☐ Flush to cover up pooping sounds

☐ Reply to work emails / messages

☐ Scroll through social media

☐ Act to prevent any splashback

☐ Read through the entire guest book

Doodles & brilliant bathroom thoughts

Welcome To Our Bathroom

Rate your experience

Seat comfort ☆☆☆☆☆

Flush strength ☆☆☆☆☆

Ambience ☆☆☆☆☆

Paper quality ☆☆☆☆☆

Amenities ☆☆☆☆☆

Sound proofing ☆☆☆☆☆

Name: _____   Visiting from: _____

Date: _____   Time: _____   Duration: _____

Describe our bathroom in one word: _____

Do you scrunch or fold? Why? _____

Most memorable bathroom visited? _____

Best euphemism for performing #2? _____

Favorite bathroom activity: _____

Doodles & brilliant bathroom thoughts

During your visit did you

☐ Look in the medicine cabinet

☐ Check out your butt in the mirror

☐ Flush to cover up pooping sounds

☐ Reply to work emails / messages

☐ Scroll through social media

☐ Act to prevent any splashback

☐ Read through the entire guest book

Welcome To Our Bathroom

Name: _____ Visiting from: _____

Date: _____ Time: _____ Duration: _____

Describe our bathroom in one word: _____

Do you scrunch or fold? Why? _____

Most memorable bathroom visited? _____

Best euphemism for performing #2? _____

Favorite bathroom activity: _____

Rate your experience

Seat comfort ☆ ☆ ☆ ☆ ☆

Flush strength ☆ ☆ ☆ ☆ ☆

Ambience ☆ ☆ ☆ ☆ ☆

Paper quality ☆ ☆ ☆ ☆ ☆

Amenities ☆ ☆ ☆ ☆ ☆

Sound proofing ☆ ☆ ☆ ☆ ☆

During your visit did you

☐ Look in the medicine cabinet

☐ Check out your butt in the mirror

☐ Flush to cover up pooping sounds

☐ Reply to work emails / messages

☐ Scroll through social media

☐ Act to prevent any splashback

☐ Read through the entire guest book

Doodles & brilliant bathroom thoughts

Welcome To Our Bathroom

Rate your experience

Seat comfort ☆☆☆☆☆

Flush strength ☆☆☆☆☆

Ambience ☆☆☆☆☆

Paper quality ☆☆☆☆☆

Amenities ☆☆☆☆☆

Sound proofing ☆☆☆☆☆

Name: _____ Visiting from: _____

Date: _____ Time: _____ Duration: _____

Describe our bathroom in one word: _____

Do you scrunch or fold? Why? _____

Most memorable bathroom visited? _____

Best euphemism for performing #2? _____

Favorite bathroom activity: _____

Doodles & brilliant bathroom thoughts

During your visit did you

☐ Look in the medicine cabinet

☐ Check out your butt in the mirror

☐ Flush to cover up pooping sounds

☐ Reply to work emails / messages

☐ Scroll through social media

☐ Act to prevent any splashback

☐ Read through the entire guest book

Welcome To Our Bathroom

Name: _____ Visiting from: _____

Date: _____ Time: _____ Duration: _____

Describe our bathroom in one word: _____

Do you scrunch or fold? Why? _____

Most memorable bathroom visited? _____

Best euphemism for performing #2? _____

Favorite bathroom activity: _____

Rate your experience

Seat comfort	☆ ☆ ☆ ☆ ☆
Flush strength	☆ ☆ ☆ ☆ ☆
Ambience	☆ ☆ ☆ ☆ ☆
Paper quality	☆ ☆ ☆ ☆ ☆
Amenities	☆ ☆ ☆ ☆ ☆
Sound proofing	☆ ☆ ☆ ☆ ☆

During your visit did you

- ☐ Look in the medicine cabinet
- ☐ Check out your butt in the mirror
- ☐ Flush to cover up pooping sounds
- ☐ Reply to work emails / messages
- ☐ Scroll through social media
- ☐ Act to prevent any splashback
- ☐ Read through the entire guest book

Doodles & brilliant bathroom thoughts

Welcome To Our Bathroom

Rate your experience

Seat comfort ☆ ☆ ☆ ☆ ☆

Flush strength ☆ ☆ ☆ ☆ ☆

Ambience ☆ ☆ ☆ ☆ ☆

Paper quality ☆ ☆ ☆ ☆ ☆

Amenities ☆ ☆ ☆ ☆ ☆

Sound proofing ☆ ☆ ☆ ☆ ☆

Name: _____   Visiting from: _____

Date: _____   Time: _____   Duration: _____

Describe our bathroom in one word: _____

Do you scrunch or fold? Why? _____

Most memorable bathroom visited? _____

Best euphemism for performing #2? _____

Favorite bathroom activity: _____

Doodles & brilliant bathroom thoughts

During your visit did you

☐ Look in the medicine cabinet

☐ Check out your butt in the mirror

☐ Flush to cover up pooping sounds

☐ Reply to work emails / messages

☐ Scroll through social media

☐ Act to prevent any splashback

☐ Read through the entire guest book

Welcome To Our Bathroom

Name: _____ Visiting from: _____

Date: _____ Time: _____ Duration: _____

Describe our bathroom in one word: _____

Do you scrunch or fold? Why? _____

Most memorable bathroom visited? _____

Best euphemism for performing #2? _____

Favorite bathroom activity: _____

Rate your experience

Seat comfort ☆ ☆ ☆ ☆ ☆

Flush strength ☆ ☆ ☆ ☆ ☆

Ambience ☆ ☆ ☆ ☆ ☆

Paper quality ☆ ☆ ☆ ☆ ☆

Amenities ☆ ☆ ☆ ☆ ☆

Sound proofing ☆ ☆ ☆ ☆ ☆

During your visit did you

☐ Look in the medicine cabinet

☐ Check out your butt in the mirror

☐ Flush to cover up pooping sounds

☐ Reply to work emails / messages

☐ Scroll through social media

☐ Act to prevent any splashback

☐ Read through the entire guest book

Doodles & brilliant bathroom thoughts

Welcome To Our Bathroom

Rate your experience

Seat comfort ☆☆☆☆☆

Flush strength ☆☆☆☆☆

Ambience ☆☆☆☆☆

Paper quality ☆☆☆☆☆

Amenities ☆☆☆☆☆

Sound proofing ☆☆☆☆☆

Name: _____ Visiting from: _____

Date: _____ Time: _____ Duration: _____

Describe our bathroom in one word: _____

Do you scrunch or fold? Why? _____

Most memorable bathroom visited? _____

Best euphemism for performing #2? _____

Favorite bathroom activity: _____

Doodles & brilliant bathroom thoughts

During your visit did you

☐ Look in the medicine cabinet

☐ Check out your butt in the mirror

☐ Flush to cover up pooping sounds

☐ Reply to work emails / messages

☐ Scroll through social media

☐ Act to prevent any splashback

☐ Read through the entire guest book

Welcome To Our Bathroom

Name: _____ Visiting from: _____

Date: _____ Time: _____ Duration: _____

Describe our bathroom in one word: _____

Do you scrunch or fold? Why? _____

Most memorable bathroom visited? _____

Best euphemism for performing #2? _____

Favorite bathroom activity: _____

Rate your experience

Seat comfort ☆ ☆ ☆ ☆ ☆

Flush strength ☆ ☆ ☆ ☆ ☆

Ambience ☆ ☆ ☆ ☆ ☆

Paper quality ☆ ☆ ☆ ☆ ☆

Amenities ☆ ☆ ☆ ☆ ☆

Sound proofing ☆ ☆ ☆ ☆ ☆

During your visit did you

☐ Look in the medicine cabinet

☐ Check out your butt in the mirror

☐ Flush to cover up pooping sounds

☐ Reply to work emails / messages

☐ Scroll through social media

☐ Act to prevent any splashback

☐ Read through the entire guest book

Doodles & brilliant bathroom thoughts

Welcome To Our Bathroom

Rate your experience

Seat comfort ☆☆☆☆☆

Flush strength ☆☆☆☆☆

Ambience ☆☆☆☆☆

Paper quality ☆☆☆☆☆

Amenities ☆☆☆☆☆

Sound proofing ☆☆☆☆☆

Name: _____ Visiting from: _____

Date: _____ Time: _____ Duration: _____

Describe our bathroom in one word: _____

Do you scrunch or fold? Why? _____

Most memorable bathroom visited? _____

Best euphemism for performing #2? _____

Favorite bathroom activity: _____

Doodles & brilliant bathroom thoughts

During your visit did you

☐ Look in the medicine cabinet

☐ Check out your butt in the mirror

☐ Flush to cover up pooping sounds

☐ Reply to work emails / messages

☐ Scroll through social media

☐ Act to prevent any splashback

☐ Read through the entire guest book

Welcome To Our Bathroom

Name: _____ Visiting from: _____

Date: _____ Time: _____ Duration: _____

Describe our bathroom in one word: _____

Do you scrunch or fold? Why? _____

Most memorable bathroom visited? _____

Best euphemism for performing #2? _____

Favorite bathroom activity: _____

Rate your experience

Seat comfort ☆ ☆ ☆ ☆ ☆

Flush strength ☆ ☆ ☆ ☆ ☆

Ambience ☆ ☆ ☆ ☆ ☆

Paper quality ☆ ☆ ☆ ☆ ☆

Amenities ☆ ☆ ☆ ☆ ☆

Sound proofing ☆ ☆ ☆ ☆ ☆

During your visit did you

☐ Look in the medicine cabinet

☐ Check out your butt in the mirror

☐ Flush to cover up pooping sounds

☐ Reply to work emails / messages

☐ Scroll through social media

☐ Act to prevent any splashback

☐ Read through the entire guest book

Doodles & brilliant bathroom thoughts

Welcome To Our Bathroom

Rate your experience

Seat comfort ☆☆☆☆☆

Flush strength ☆☆☆☆☆

Ambience ☆☆☆☆☆

Paper quality ☆☆☆☆☆

Amenities ☆☆☆☆☆

Sound proofing ☆☆☆☆☆

Name: _____ Visiting from: _____

Date: _____ Time: _____ Duration: _____

Describe our bathroom in one word: _____

Do you scrunch or fold? Why? _____

Most memorable bathroom visited? _____

Best euphemism for performing #2? _____

Favorite bathroom activity: _____

Doodles & brilliant bathroom thoughts

During your visit did you

☐ Look in the medicine cabinet

☐ Check out your butt in the mirror

☐ Flush to cover up pooping sounds

☐ Reply to work emails / messages

☐ Scroll through social media

☐ Act to prevent any splashback

☐ Read through the entire guest book

Welcome To Our Bathroom

Name: _____ Visiting from: _____

Date: _____ Time: _____ Duration: _____

Describe our bathroom in one word: _____

Do you scrunch or fold? Why? _____

Most memorable bathroom visited? _____

Best euphemism for performing #2? _____

Favorite bathroom activity: _____

Rate your experience

Seat comfort   ☆ ☆ ☆ ☆ ☆

Flush strength   ☆ ☆ ☆ ☆ ☆

Ambience   ☆ ☆ ☆ ☆ ☆

Paper quality   ☆ ☆ ☆ ☆ ☆

Amenities   ☆ ☆ ☆ ☆ ☆

Sound proofing   ☆ ☆ ☆ ☆ ☆

During your visit did you

☐ Look in the medicine cabinet

☐ Check out your butt in the mirror

☐ Flush to cover up pooping sounds

☐ Reply to work emails / messages

☐ Scroll through social media

☐ Act to prevent any splashback

☐ Read through the entire guest book

Doodles & brilliant bathroom thoughts

Welcome To Our Bathroom

Rate your experience

Seat comfort ☆☆☆☆☆

Flush strength ☆☆☆☆☆

Ambience ☆☆☆☆☆

Paper quality ☆☆☆☆☆

Amenities ☆☆☆☆☆

Sound proofing ☆☆☆☆☆

Name: _____ Visiting from: _____

Date: _____ Time: _____ Duration: _____

Describe our bathroom in one word: _____

Do you scrunch or fold? Why? _____

Most memorable bathroom visited? _____

Best euphemism for performing #2? _____

Favorite bathroom activity: _____

Doodles & brilliant bathroom thoughts

During your visit did you

☐ Look in the medicine cabinet

☐ Check out your butt in the mirror

☐ Flush to cover up pooping sounds

☐ Reply to work emails / messages

☐ Scroll through social media

☐ Act to prevent any splashback

☐ Read through the entire guest book

Welcome To Our Bathroom

Name: _____ Visiting from: _____

Date: _____ Time: _____ Duration: _____

Describe our bathroom in one word: _____

Do you scrunch or fold? Why? _____

Most memorable bathroom visited? _____

Best euphemism for performing #2? _____

Favorite bathroom activity: _____

Rate your experience

Seat comfort	☆ ☆ ☆ ☆ ☆
Flush strength	☆ ☆ ☆ ☆ ☆
Ambience	☆ ☆ ☆ ☆ ☆
Paper quality	☆ ☆ ☆ ☆ ☆
Amenities	☆ ☆ ☆ ☆ ☆
Sound proofing	☆ ☆ ☆ ☆ ☆

During your visit did you

- ☐ Look in the medicine cabinet
- ☐ Check out your butt in the mirror
- ☐ Flush to cover up pooping sounds
- ☐ Reply to work emails / messages
- ☐ Scroll through social media
- ☐ Act to prevent any splashback
- ☐ Read through the entire guest book

Doodles & brilliant bathroom thoughts

Welcome To Our Bathroom

Rate your experience

Seat comfort ☆ ☆ ☆ ☆ ☆

Flush strength ☆ ☆ ☆ ☆ ☆

Ambience ☆ ☆ ☆ ☆ ☆

Paper quality ☆ ☆ ☆ ☆ ☆

Amenities ☆ ☆ ☆ ☆ ☆

Sound proofing ☆ ☆ ☆ ☆ ☆

Name: _____ Visiting from: _____

Date: _____ Time: _____ Duration: _____

Describe our bathroom in one word: _____

Do you scrunch or fold? Why? _____

Most memorable bathroom visited? _____

Best euphemism for performing #2? _____

Favorite bathroom activity: _____

Doodles & brilliant bathroom thoughts

During your visit did you

☐ Look in the medicine cabinet

☐ Check out your butt in the mirror

☐ Flush to cover up pooping sounds

☐ Reply to work emails / messages

☐ Scroll through social media

☐ Act to prevent any splashback

☐ Read through the entire guest book

Welcome To Our Bathroom

Name: _____   Visiting from: _____

Date: _____   Time: _____   Duration: _____

Describe our bathroom in one word: _____

Do you scrunch or fold? Why? _____

Most memorable bathroom visited? _____

Best euphemism for performing #2? _____

Favorite bathroom activity: _____

Rate your experience

Seat comfort ☆ ☆ ☆ ☆ ☆

Flush strength ☆ ☆ ☆ ☆ ☆

Ambience ☆ ☆ ☆ ☆ ☆

Paper quality ☆ ☆ ☆ ☆ ☆

Amenities ☆ ☆ ☆ ☆ ☆

Sound proofing ☆ ☆ ☆ ☆ ☆

During your visit did you

☐ Look in the medicine cabinet

☐ Check out your butt in the mirror

☐ Flush to cover up pooping sounds

☐ Reply to work emails / messages

☐ Scroll through social media

☐ Act to prevent any splashback

☐ Read through the entire guest book

Doodles & brilliant bathroom thoughts

Made in the USA
Middletown, DE
23 November 2022